CIRIA C650

London, 2005

Environmental good practice on site

(Second edition)

Greg Chant-Hall

Philip Charles, Samantha Connolly (*Eds*)

CIRIA

sharing knowledge
building best practice

Classic House, 174–180 Old Street, London EC1V 9BP
Telephone +44 (0)20 7549 3300
Fax +44 (0)20 7253 0523
Email enquiries@ciria.org
Website www.ciria.org

Environmental good practice on site (Second edition)

This second edition of the *Environmental good practice on site* handbook (C650), updates the previous version (C502,1999), which resulted from CIRIA research project 559. This update has been undertaken in collaboration with a Project Steering Group of industry practitioners and was funded by the CIRIA Core Programme and the Environment Agency. See Acknowledgements (Appendices 6 and 7).

Environmental good practice on site
Second edition 2005.

CIRIA

Charles, P and Connolly, S (*Eds*)

CIRIA C650   © CIRIA 2005   ISBN 0-86017-650-9

First printed 1999 as C502. Reprinted 2000, 2001, 2002; revised 2003.

Keywords		
Environmental good practice, pollution prevention, recycling and reclaimed materials, regulation, risk and value management, site management, supply chain management, sustainable construction, sustainable resource use, waste minimisation, water quality, water resources		
Reader interest	**Classification**	
Contractors, site workers, site managers, engineers supervisors, architects	Availability Content Status Users	unrestricted advice/guidance committee-guided construction professionals and managers

British Library Cataloguing in Publication Data
A catalogue record is available for this book from the British Library.

Published by CIRIA, Classic House, 174–180 Old Street, London EC1V 9BP, UK.

Summary

Construction activities will always have an impact on the surrounding environment and neighbours. Good environmental practice enables these impacts to be managed positively. Impacts take many forms, for example effects on surrounding flora and fauna, watercourses, noise or pollution. Clients, their professional advisers, contractors and the whole construction supply chain, all have responsibilities for environmental management.

This handbook provides practical guidance about managing construction on site to control environmental impacts, and is relevant to all concerned with the construction process. The handbook has four sections:

1   Benefits and obligations

    Outlining the benefits of good practice and the environmental obligations under which a site operates in terms of both the legislation and the contract conditions.

2   General site management issues

    Providing general guidance on good site practice to provide the framework for managing environmental impacts.

3   Environmental issues

    Providing guidance on how to manage impacts for each environmental issue and how to recognise and deal with any problems that may arise.

4   Construction processes

    Identifying the environmental issues that need to be considered when carrying out a particular construction process.

This handbook is intended as a user-friendly guide, reference and training aid, replacing CIRIA publication C502, *Environmental good practice on site*. It is accompanied by a pocket-sized book containing a series of on-site checklists (C651) *Environmental good practice – pocket book*, and tool box talks (on CD), which contain key advice for all site personnel.

The accompanying CD includes further reference material.

Contents

Contents

The target audience

This handbook provides guidance on environmental good practice for each construction stage and is aimed primarily at site personnel including sub-contractors. People involved in the early stages of a project's development, including designers and planners, can influence the ability of the site personnel to meet their obligations.

Primary audience	Secondary audience
• site managers • site engineers • site foremen and site supervisors • project managers • contract supervisors/resident engineers • site environmental coordinator	• client organisations • estimators • quantity surveyors • company directors • designers • construction planners.

The nature of environmental legislation is changing and this in itself, together with changes in good practice, makes this handbook relevant for all levels of construction experience.

How to use this handbook

This handbook is intended be used on site following the completion of site investigation that may have involved Environmental Impact Assessment (EIA) and Strategic Environmental Assessment (SEA). The findings from these assessments should be referred to, as the issues they highlight could impact on the progress of a project.

This publication is written for a wide range of construction personnel. Section 1 presents the benefits of reading this handbook and the reasons for adopting good environmental practice on site.

Good environmental practice starts with planning for good site management. Section 2 explains how the overall establishment and management of the site can form the basis of environmental good practice. Therefore those with management responsibility, from the beginning of the set-up of the site through to project completion and demobilisation, should read this section.

If you want to know about a particular environmental issue (eg noise or archaeology), then turn to Section 3 for guidance. If you need to know what environmental issues to consider for a particular construction process (eg piling), then turn to that process in Section 4.

Use this handbook with the toolbox talks (on the accompanying CD) by concentrating on the issue or construction activity most relevant to the work taking place at that time.

Throughout the handbook symbols alongside the text help identify the type of information presented. These symbols and their explanations are shown below.

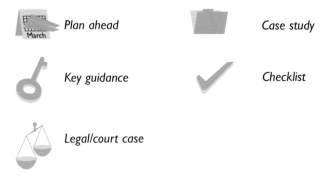

Plan ahead

Case study

Key guidance

Checklist

Legal/court case

Coverage of this handbook

This handbook updates CIRIA publication C502, *Environmental good practice on site*. It addresses environmental issues once a project has reached the construction stage. For each of the key topics it describes the issues and how to avoid or overcome them. To facilitate good environmental practice on site, this handbook explains how to establish a suitable management framework for the site, and how to set up central site facilities such as vehicle refuelling stations and materials storage locations.

The reader should be clear about the limitations in the scope of the handbook. In particular:

● it is not a health and safety manual

● it must not replace contact with regulators

● although it gives an overview of legislation, detailed guidance should be sought from the company's environmental representative (or external specialists) if it is required

● in all instances, when dealing with the issues covered, do not take action beyond your expertise. If in doubt, seek specialist advice

● it does not deal with environmental issues that should be covered during the planning and design of the project.

The guidance is generally relevant for all types of contract conditions, eg traditional, design and build, design-build-finance-operate (DBFO) and build-operate-transfer (BOT).

However, the site manager should be aware that, on some types of contract, the contractor carries the risk of cost or programme delays caused by unexpected events or finds. If in doubt seek advice from your quantity surveyor or contracts manager.

Relationship to other CIRIA guidance

CIRIA has produced three key publications that establish the environmental issues to be addressed at all stages of construction:

- *A clients' guide to greener construction* (SP120)
- *Environmental handbook for building and civil and engineering projects: design and specification* (SP97)
- *Environmental handbook for building and civil and engineering projects: Vol. 2 construction phase* (SP98).

These key publications outline the issues, principles and legislation that should be adopted to improve environmental performance in the construction industry. Details of other CIRIA publications of particular relevance can be found in Appendix 4.

Abatement notices   A local authority has powers, under the **Environmental Protection Act 1990**, to serve an Abatement Notice where it is satisfied that a statutory nuisance exists.

Abstraction   The removal of water from groundwaters or surface waters, either temporarily or permanently. Licences are required from the Environment Agency in England and Wales. No licence required in Scotland though this is likely to change under the requirement of the **Water Services and Water Environment (Scotland) Act 2003**.

Asbestos   Environmental legislation looks to control pollution arising from manufacturing industry, demolition works, asbestos waste disposal and transportation of asbestos.

Biodiversity   The entire variety of life on earth; this means species, genetic variations within species, and the communities, habitats and ecosystems and habitats within which they occur.

Brownfield site   As opposed to a "greenfield" site, a brownfield site is a generic term for land used previously for an industrial or commercial purpose, being available for redevelopment towards new industrial, commercial or residential use. The level of remediation or clean-up necessary may vary hugely.

Consent (discharge)   A statutory document issued by the Environment Agency under Schedule 10 of the **Water Resources Act 1991** or the Scottish Environment Protection Agency under the **Control of Pollution Act 1974** to indicate any limits and conditions on the discharge of an effluent to controlled water. Contact EHSNI for equivalent legislation for Northern Ireland.

Controlled waters   Virtually all natural waters in the UK. This includes surface water (rivers, streams, lakes, reservoirs, ditches, ponds), including those temporarily dry, and groundwater (aquifers), as well as coastal waters up to three miles out. It is an offence to pollute such waters. Responsibility for policing controlled waters is placed with the regulators.

Glossary

Contaminated land   Land which contains substances likely to represent a hazard to human beings, animals or the environment.

Discharge consents (Water)   Any intended discharge to or abstraction of water from "controlled waters" will require prior permission from the environmental regulator over granting of a consent. Any intended discharge to foul sewer will require negotiation with the relevant water company for a consent.

Dust   Airborne solid matter up to about 2 mm in size. Along with noise and odour, dust is probably the most common form of "nuisance".

Duty of care for waste   Legally set by Section 34 of the **Environmental Protection Act 1990**. This imposes a duty on everyone in the waste management chain, ie anyone who imports, carries, produces, keeps, treats, or disposes of waste or acts as a broker.

Ecology   All living things, such as trees, flowering plants, insects, birds and mammals, and their habitats.

Enforcement notices   Issued under the **Water Resources Act 1991** by the Environment Agency or **Control of Pollution Act 1974** (as amended) by SEPA, if the discharge consent holder is contravening the conditions of the consent. Contact EHSNI for equivalent legislation for Northern Ireland.

Environmental impact   The total effect of any operation on the environment.

Environmental indicator   A measure, which can be used to assess the present state of the environment by looking at trends over time.

European Waste Catalogue   Lists various types of waste, eg Cat. 17 00 00 – Construction and Demolition Waste

Forest Stewardship Council   Based in Mexico, the organisation sets out international standards for the responsible management of forests in accordance with ecological, social and economic criteria.

Global warming	The projected consequences of the greenhouse effect arising out of man's industrial practices, use of transport and domestic lifestyle. There is growing evidence that this is a reality and not just a cyclic natural effect.
Greenhouse gases	Natural and man-made gases which influence the greenhouse effect. Including carbon dioxide, methane, ozone and chlorofluorocarbons.
Greywater	The capture and reuse of lightly contaminated water for a second purpose eg water from wash handbasins used to flush toilets.
Groundwater	Water beneath the ground's surface.
Groundwater protection zones	Identifies the proximity of land to a groundwater source.
Heritage bodies	These have a general duty to conserve our heritage, to carry out scheduling of historic remains, and to undertake research. They comprise English Heritage, Cadw, Historic Scotland, and the Environment and Heritage Service Northern Ireland.
Landfill tax	Introduced in October 1996, as a tax payable to HM Customs & Excise by the operator, on all active waste materials going to landfill. Rising by £3 per tonne per year the tax is currently £18 per tonne (from April 2005) for active waste. Inert wastes are now not subject to the tax. There are certain defined exemptions.
Local Biodiversity Action Plan	An LBAP is used by local authorities and others to identify environmental objectives and targets. Aimed at ensuring sustainable development in relation to processes such as planning, the LBAP helps conserve and save valuable habitats as well as plant or animal species. LBAPs link to a National Biodiversity Plan set by government.
Local planning authorities	Based within local councils, the LPA is responsible for local planning issues including control of building works and development of land, protection of hedgerows and trees, and listed buildings.

Glossary

Mitigation	Refers to the environmental impact of scheme's development or operation and the actions, which may be taken to reduce or ameliorate such impacts.
Nature conservancy bodies	Countryside Council for Wales, English Nature (Natural England from October 2006), Environment and Heritage Service Northern Ireland, and Scottish Natural Heritage that have regional responsibility for promoting the conservation of wildlife and natural features in the UK.
Noise	Often explained as being a sound that is not desired. Sound is a wave motion carried by air particles between the source and the receiver, usually the ear.
Noise abatement zones	Local authorities have the power to set up a noise abatement zone as an area-based approach for controlling commercial and industrial noise
Polluter pays principle	Not defined in law, but which requires those who cause pollution or environmental damage, to pay the costs of preventing, reducing, or remediating any pollution or damage.
Pollution	The introduction of a substance that has the potential to cause harm to the environment or any other living organisms supported by the environment. Pollutants include silty water, oils, chemicals, litter and mud.
Prescribed processes	Any activities carried out on premises or by means of mobile plant (eg concrete crusher) capable of causing pollution to the environment. Nearly always require a local authority (SEPA in Scotland) licence.
Recycling	Collecting and separating materials from waste and processing them to produce useable products
Reduction of waste	Waste reduction has two components: • reducing the amount of waste produced • reducing the hazard of the waste produced.
Remediation notice(s)	Having identified any contaminated land within its area, the environmental regulator or the local authority may serve on an "appropriate person" such a notice, specifying what needs to be done and the timescale for it to be done.

14

Section 60 notice	Issued under the **Control of Pollution Act 1974** to control noise pollution and nuisance. If issued the conditions must be complied with until revoked or successfully appealed against
Section 61 consent	Issued under the **Control of Pollution Act 1974** to permit noise on site.
Sewage provider	Regional water utility company or Scottish Water responsible as the drainage authority for removal and treatment of foul water/sewage. Overseen by EHSNI in Northern Ireland.
Statutory consultees	Organisations that must be consulted at the planning stage of projects. These organisations include regulators, heritage bodies and nature conservation bodies
Sustainable development	"Development that meets the needs of the present without compromising the ability of future generations to meet their own needs" (from the Bruntland Report).
Sustainable timber	Wood that is obtained from a sustainably managed forest.
Transfer note	Required under the **Environmental Protection (Duty of Care) Regulations** as a legal document describing the transfer of controlled/directive waste between dutyholders.
Transfer station	Facility where waste is transferred from collection vehicles to larger vehicles or onto rail or river for onward transport for disposal.
Waste	Any substance or object that the holder discards, intends to discard, or is required to discard. ● controlled waste – household, commercial and industrial waste ● directive waste – material that the holder discards ● difficult waste – includes liquids and sludges ● inert waste – eg clean bricks, blocks, concrete ● non-hazardous waste – a Landfill Tax classification ● hazardous waste – hazardous or dangerous to life.

Glossary

Waste hierarchy	• eliminate • reduce • reuse • recycle • recover • disposal (landfill only as last resort).
Waste minimisation/ resource efficiency	The reduction of waste at source by understanding and changing processes to minimise its production. It includes the substitution of less environmentally harmful materials in the production process.
Water protection zones	The Secretary of State for the Environment has the power to declare a Water Protection Zone, to protect specific controlled waters. Declaration of a zone may prevent or severely restrict any activities placing the zone at risk.
Wildlife corridor	A linear habitat, or range of habitats in which species can survive, and along which they can move to other wildlife areas. Examples include rivers and streams, hedges and shelterbelts, field and road margins.

CIRIA C650

Acronyms and abbreviations

ACE	Association of Consulting Engineers
AONB	Area of Outstanding Natural Beauty
ASSI	Area of Special Scientific Interest (in Northern Ireland)
BPM	Best Practicable Means
BPN	Building Preservation Notice
BRE	Building Research Establishment
BREEAM	Building Research Establishment Environmental Assessment Method.
BS	British Standard
Cadw	Welsh Historic Monuments
CCTV	Closed Circuit Television
CCW	Countryside Council for Wales
CECA	Civil Engineering Contractors Association
CEEQUAL	Civil Engineering Environmental Quality Assessment and Award Scheme
CLR	Contaminated Land Report
COPA	Control of Pollution Act
COSHH	The Control of Substances Hazardous to Health (Regulations 1994)
CWS	County Wildlife Sites
DARD	Department of Agriculture and Rural Development (Northern Ireland)
dB	Decibel
Defra	Department of Environment Food and Rural Affairs
DTI	Department of Trade and Industry
EHNSI	Environment and Heritage Service Northern Ireland
EIA	Environmental Impact Assessment
EMAS	Eco-management and Audit Scheme
EMP	Environmental Management Plan
EMS	Environmental Management System
EnCams	Environmental Campaigns
EPA	Environmental Protection Act 1990
EWC	European Waste Catalogue
FOD	Foreign Object Damage
FSC	Forest Stewardship Council
HSE	Health & Safety Executive

Acronyms and abbreviations

ICE	Institution of Civil Engineers
IFA	Institute of Field Archaeologists
ISO	International Standards Organisation.
LAPC	Local Air Pollution Control
LBAP	Local Biodiversity Action Plan
LNR	Local Nature Reserve
MCERTS	Monitoring Certification Scheme
MDF	Medium Density Fibreboard
NNR	National Nature Reserve
NRSWA	New Roads and Streets Works Act 1991
PEFC	Programme for Endorsement of Forest Certification
PFA	Pulverised Fly Ash
PPE	Personal Protective Equipment
PVC	Polyvinyl Chloride
RAMSAR	Wetlands of international importance
RIGS	Regionally Important Geological Sites
RSPB	Royal Society for the Protection of Birds
SAC	Special Areas of Conservation
SEA	Strategic Environmental Assessment
SEMP	Site Environmental Management Plan
SEPA	Scottish Environment Protection Agency
SINC's	Sites of Importance for Nature Conservation
SMC	Scheduled Monument Consent
SNCI	Sites of Nature Conservation Interest
SPA	Special Protection Area
SSSI	Sites of Special Scientific Interest
SWMP	Site Waste Management Plan
TMP	Traffic Management Plan
TPO	Tree Preservation Order
UKAS	United Kingdom Accreditation Service
WAC	Waste Acceptance Criteria
WEEE	Waste Electrical and Electronic Equipment
WEWS	Water Environment and Water Services (Scotland) Act 2003
WRAP	Waste and Resources Action Programme
WWF	World Wildlife Fund

Construction sites are often criticised for the impacts that they have on the surrounding environment and residents. These impacts include; effects on flora and fauna, excess noise and water, air and ground pollution. Good environmental practice on site to manage these impacts must be a high priority.

Increasingly efforts are being made within the construction industry to implement environmental improvements:

- clients are requesting evidence of environmental credentials from contractors before awarding contracts
- contractors are assisting their suppliers and sub-contractors to manage and improve the environmental performance of their own operations
- top level commitment is demonstrated by environmental policies
- many construction companies have an environmental management system (EMS) and report on environmental and sustainability issues
- on-site personnel are implementing many environmental initiatives.

Action is still needed to improve environmental performance as the construction industry causes more water pollution incidents than any other industry. There are many incentives for improving performance, which include:

- enhanced environmental conditions resulting from good practice
- effective risk management to avoid the cost implications of failing to meet environmental obligations, regulations and legislation
- resource efficiency to maximise achievable cost savings
- demonstrating benefits of good environmental performance to interested parties including clients, regulators and the public.

1.1 The benefits of good practice

"Sustainability" and "sustainable development" are terms defined differently by different people. The original definition (and the one still most widely used), was made in the Bruntland Report *Our common future* (World Commission on Environment and Development, 1987), which defined it as:

> *"Development that meets the needs of the present without compromising the ability of future generations to meet their own needs".*

In March 2005 the UK Government introduced its new strategy for sustainable development; *Securing the future – delivering UK sustainable development strategy*. The strategy contains five principles with an explicit focus on environmental limits. Further details on the strategy are available at: www.sustainable-development.gov.uk

Environmental benefits

- reduced damage to the surrounding air, water resources, land and to fauna and flora from potentially damaging activities
- reduced demand for resources through better material selection, procurement and management, less wastage and greater use of recycled, reclaimed and sustainably sourced materials.

Social benefits

- reduced nuisance to neighbours by liaising with the local community before and during the project to keep them informed about works that could affect them.

Economic benefits

- improved opportunities to tender through demonstration of sound environmental performance and effective risk management
- less money wasted on fines for non-compliance with legislation and associated costs of clean-up, legal fees and management time
- fewer delays to the project by fully characterising the site before works start, reducing costs incurred by delayed surveys
- less money lost through wasted resources that need to be disposed of to landfill

- improved environmental profile by establishing good relationships with environmental regulators and the local authority.

Benefits are felt at both a corporate and a project level. So what do they mean to the individual?

- the site manager can demonstrate improved margins
- the site engineer's workload can be reduced by fewer conflicts
- reduced risk of complaints
- reduced bad/negative press locally
- avoidance of delays.

1.2 Environmental obligations

There are a number of controls that ensure good practice is followed, and have both legislative and contractual origins and include:

Contract conditions

These address any conditions imposed through the planning system and commitments made to the local communities, and may include provisions made after an environmental assessment. Non-compliance will be penalised through the contract.

National legislation

It is enforced primarily by the environmental regulators to protect both the natural environment and residents surrounding sites. Key legislation includes the **Environmental Protection Act 1990** and the **Water Resources Act 1991**.

Other legislation is in place to protect specific features of the environment; with sites being designated and protected by virtue of their ecological, archaeological, geological or geomorphological importance.

Court convictions can lead to unlimited fines for a company and/or imprisonment or community service for the person (individual and/or appropriate director) or company responsible, if it is found that suitable training, procedures or equipment were not being provided.

1.2 Environmental obligations

Local control

Local authorities can impose a number of requirements through the powers given to them by national legislation including noise and air controls. Planning legislation at both a local and national level is the main control on construction development covering many aspects including scale and traffic.

Corporate control

Many contractors have corporate environmental policies and an EMS which employees are required to follow. There may be a specific site environmental management plan (SEMP) for a project that stipulates controls to minimise environmental damage.

2.1 The management framework

This section outlines a framework for managing the environment on site. Steps 1 to 5 below should be followed for every site.

2.1.1 Setting the scene

Effective environmental management on site requires a team effort. This includes inputs from the main contractor and sub-contractors on site, the contractors' organisation off site, designers, clients and suppliers. To manage this teamwork effectively the **site manager** should follow the steps outlined below. So should the managers of any sub-contractor on site that has the potential to cause environmental effects through its activities – which applies to all trades and operations.

STEP 1 **– Identify the environmental obligations of the project**

- identify legal obligations
- identify environmental requirements contained in the project brief, specification or contract documents. This should include a review of any Environmental Impact Assessment, Environmental Statement or other client/designer derived assessment.

STEP 2 **– Identify the environmental risks (including emergencies) particular to the site**

- review relevant documentation identified in Step 1 (see Section 1.2)
- talk to environmental regulators about their concerns for the site at an early stage
- liaise with clients and designers to establish how they can help identify and overcome potential environmental difficulties (see Section 2.1.6)
- compile a risk register for the site
- during site induction alert all site personnel to the risks associated with the construction on site.

STEP 3 – Identify environmental responsibilities

- define the environmental responsibilities of all personnel working on site, including those who are involved in implementing and monitoring initiatives (see Section 2.1.3)

- define lines of communication between site personnel, and those responsible for producing the site environmental plan (see below).

March

> The better responsibilities are defined and understood the more likely they are to be implemented.

STEP 4 – Establish an environmental management plan (EMP)

- information gathered in Steps 1 to 3 can be used to form the basis of an Environmental Management System (EMS). The core document of an EMS is an (EMP)

- the most important features of an EMP is that it is site specific, accessible, regularly revised and in constant use

- the site EMP can be used to develop method statements for specific components of work

- method statements are key documents on site as these will be referenced during the process and will incorporate not only environmental, but also all other requirements eg health and safety and buildability

- a site waste management plan (SWMP) must be developed as part of the site EMP

- Section 2.1.7 outlines how the site EMP can fit into the environmental management system of the company.

STEP 5 – Monitoring and follow up

- a robust monitoring system should be implemented to ensure you are meeting the requirements of your EMP

- all monitoring data should be retained so there is an auditable trail

- monitoring refers to a wide range of activities, including:
  - audit reports
  - maintaining and reviewing training records
  - chemical analysis of discharges and nearby streams
  - waste transfer notes
  - records of dust generation
  - noise monitoring records.

- measures must be put in place to rectify any non-compliance with your EMP that is raised during monitoring

- monitoring will provide baseline data, which can be used for setting objectives and targets.

2.1.2 Dealing with regulators

Whatever the size of the project it will be necessary to deal with environmental regulators. Regulators have a diverse range of specific responsibilities and powers to enforce legislation. Their responsibilities are described below.

Regulator	Responsibilities
Local authority	Noise, air quality, traffic, the planning process and contaminated land
Environmental regulators	Discharges to land and controlled waters, waste, water abstraction control, nature conservation, ground and water contamination and built heritage (only in NI)
Nature conservation organisations	Designated ecological sites, geological and geomorphological sites and protected species
Heritage bodies	Designated archaeological and heritage sites
County archaeologist	Designated archaeological and heritage sites
Health and Safety Executive	Health and safety including vibration and asbestos
Water and sewerage provider	Effluent discharge to public sewer

Full contact details for and responsibilities of key national regulators and heritage bodies are given in Appendix 1.

Regulators welcome an early approach and may be able to advise on environmental issues of local importance that need to be included in the site EMP. This is particularly relevant on projects where an environmental statement has not been produced (ie the vast majority), and is often required even when an environment statement is available.

It is important to develop a constructive dialogue with regulators to ensure they are aware of what is happening on the project and why.

Checklist – Dealing with regulators	
Plan ahead and give regulators advanced warning of potential problems	
Give regulators the time they need to process your enquiry	
Always display the relevant emergency number – 0800 80 70 60 for the regulators	
Ensure site personnel know the correct procedures for reporting incidents	
Always notify the environmental regulator of any reportable contamination	

2.1.3 Environmental responsibilities

A sound approach is to ensure that environmental good practice on site starts with a commitment from company executives. Everyone on site is responsible for ensuring that their actions constitute good practice. Certain individuals have clearly defined roles as outlined below.

Individual	Role
All site personnel	Charged with following good practice and encouraged to provide feedback and suggestions for improvements. Compliance with the requirements of a site EMP
Site manager	Principal responsibility for environmental management on site including auditing environmental practice and sub-contractors, and liaising with regulators. They – or a delegated representative – will define, monitor and control environmental practice
Site engineers/foremen	Need to understand the environmental obligations and the practical measures needed to comply with them. Should review what training site personnel need and arrange for it to be provided
Middle management	Provide corporate advice on environmental legislation, good practice and company environmental policy and translate decisions into action at site level
Company executives	Responsible for directing and reviewing corporate environmental protocols and responsibilities
Client	Responsible for setting the standard for environmental management on site, which is laid down in contract requirements

Successful environmental management relies on communication. It is crucial that everyone is aware of the key issues, has the relevant information to deal with them, understands their responsibilities, and provides feedback to those in charge.

2.1.4 Sub-contractor responsibilities and the supply chain

Sub-contractors and those further down the supply chain need to understand their environmental obligations and ensure they meet them. As with any controls, environmental responsibility can be implemented with incentives or penalties. It is important for contractors and sub-contractors to work together to ensure successful delivery of projects (see checklist below for suggestions on selecting and managing sub-contractors).

Checklist – Selecting and managing sub-contractors	
Sub-contractors should present proof of their past environmental performance along with records of past and pending prosecutions	
Ensure that sub-contractors have a copy of the site EMP before commencing work	
Ensure sub-contractors attend environmental training sessions/inductions	
Ensure sub-contractors are aware of their environmental obligations on the project	
The contract should include requirements to follow good environmental practice	
Audit the performance of sub-contractors during the project	

2.1.5 Raising awareness

It is important to raise awareness of environmental issues so that people on site understand what environmental good practice is and know where to obtain information.

March

Sound environmental management comes from knowing what to do and developing the right attitudes.

Training should be used on site to disseminate good practice guidance relevant to a particular project. For a training programme to be successful, it is vital to:

- select a trainer with appropriate knowledge, skills and experience (often peer-level training is most effective)
- make training specific to the audience
- follow up and repeat training to keep abreast of changes in legislation and codes of practice.

Key aspects of training for site managers and engineers should include:

- waste management
- emergency procedures for incidents
- choice of plant
- choice of working methods
- practical actions to ensure compliance with relevant legislation
- importance of good housekeeping
- sources of advice
- personal responsibility/liability.

All site personnel should be given a site induction, including how to use a spill kit as illustrated by Figure 2.1.5. For training to be effective, adequate time should be set aside to inform people about the issues that are relevant to the site and work.

Toolbox talks can be a good way to do this (see Toolbox talks developed by the Construction Confederation Environmental Forum on the accompanying CD).

Further on-site training guidance is available from CIRIA, the Construction Confederation and environmental regulators.

Figure 2.1.5: *Spill kit training – Bovis*

2.1.6 Client and designer responsibilities

Designers should consider the environmental impact of their designs by conducting an environmental risk assessment. If it is felt that the design of temporary or permanent works compromises environmental good practice, refer it back to the designer.

Where the contract imposes environmental constraints it is worth discussing, with the designers and/or client, the reasons for the constraints. It may be possible to explore alternative approaches that have less impact (eg using recycled or secondary aggregate).

2.1.7 Environmental management systems

An environmental management system (EMS) takes a systematic approach to assessing, managing and monitoring the environmental impacts of a project. This includes the definition of management responsibilities and development of documented procedures.

There are two main international standards for EMS in use in the UK – the international standard ISO 14001 and the European standard EMAS (Eco-Management and Audit Scheme).

BS 8555 is a British Standard that provides guidance on the phased implementation of an EMS, to the ISO 14001 and EMAS standards. CIRIA has produced *Easy Access Environmental Management. Implementantion of BS 8555 in the construction sector* (C605) which provides guidance and templates for construction companies wishing to achieve either ISO 14001 or EMAS. (Also available as C606 on CD).

2.2 Planning, setting up and managing the site

This section outlines measures that should be considered when setting up and managing the site to achieve environmental good practice

2.2.1 Enabling works

Liaison with the regulator

Regulators take a proactive approach regarding environmental management on site, so it is important to involve them from an early stage in the project.

Site survey

Before any works begin, a survey needs to be carried out. The first stage should be a desk study that references the environmental risk register or online databases, for example Magic (www.magic.gov.uk), to identify any potential environmental risks. The second stage is a site survey to confirm the findings of the first stage and the identification of species that may need to be protected and relocated.

However, if is it decided that the species cannot be relocated, the contractor should go back to the designer to establish whether the scheme can be redesigned to protect the species and/or habitat.

It is important to survey a site at the correct time to allow enough lead in time to close or relocate habitats of any protected species that might be found. Refer to local biodiversity action plans (LBAPs) that can provide useful details of national and local sensitive flora, fauna and habitat types.

Site clearance

It is important to plan the site clearance at the appropriate time of year, to avoid disruption to wildlife and the associated legislation that protects various species during certain seasons. See the working with wildlife survey chart in Section 3.9 for further details. During any clearance works the burning of clearance materials should be avoided.

2.2.2 Site offices

When planning the site layout, contractors' offices and equipment should be sited to minimise visual intrusion in terms of size, colour and associated services (eg lighting) to surrounding neighbours. Hedges or existing trees can be used to screen sites and compounds in rural areas. In urban areas the construction works are usually screened with suitable hoarding (see Figure 2.3.1) or acoustic screens.

Figure 2.3.1:   *Shop front hoarding – Morrison*

There are a number of general environmental issues relating to the internal office environment including; energy usage, waste (eg paper use, toner cartridge) and the use of electrical equipment. Guidance on effective paper use is available from the Environment Agency and Envirowise including *Process improvements to reduce paper waste* (CH116).

2.2.3 Management and site control

The vast majority of environmental accidents or causes of complaints arise through ignorance, carelessness, negligence or vandalism.

A priority of the site manager is to ensure that site personnel understand that environmental issues must be taken seriously and that poor practice will not be tolerated. This can be achieved through a combination of setting a good example, rewarding good practice and punishing poor practice. Use the following checklist.

Checklist – Management and site control	
Define environmental responsibilities	
Ensure everyone on site is aware of their responsibilities and liabilities	
Through a site induction, make everyone aware of the project environmental issues and environmental standards	
Site personnel need to be aware of spill or other contamination response procedures and storage requirements	
Adequately protect site against vandalism, theft and breakage	
Ensure consent has been granted to discharge water and effluent from the site	
A drainage plan identifying foul and surface water drainage needs to be accessible	
Identify nearby rivers, streams or groundwater etc, and ensure they are inspected regularly	
Mark drains appropriately to distinguish them	
Provide fuel bunds and/or internally bunded tanks	
Provide a waste storage area	
Wheel wash or road cleaning equipment should be provided	
Indicate all designated haul routes	
Display environmental awareness posters/bulletins	
Display warning signs on site prominently	
The company environmental policy should be available for reference	

2.2.4 Managing materials

Improving the management of materials and components has environmental benefits through increased resource and site efficiency. Where site personnel follow established procedures for managing materials and components (see Section 2.4) there will be fewer incidents of spillages and contamination arising from incorrect storage or handling, and less damage to materials and components. This means less wastage of raw materials (see Section 3.7).

Checklist – Ordering and receiving deliveries	
Order the correct quantity of materials to arrive when they are needed to reduce the required storage time and risk of damage and theft	
Find out in what form materials will be delivered, so that the appropriate unloading plant can be arranged and space set aside	
Ensure deliveries are received by a member of site personnel who is able to carry out a quality inspection, and ensure that the materials are unloaded to the appropriate place and take action in the event of an accident	
Select packaging materials for deliveries that can assist effective/secure storage and movement of materials on site	
Arrange "take back" of packaging materials with suppliers	
Avoid sensitive times for deliveries, eg rush hour	

Storage

It is important to manage storage areas on site efficiently to reduce the risk of damage, injury to site personnel and theft. When storing materials keep the following points in mind:

- ensure that the suppliers' instructions are being followed

- store valuable materials, or those that are hazardous or attractive to thieves, in a secure area, out of sight of the public

- store materials away from waste storage containers and from vehicle movements that could cause accidental damage

- secure lightweight materials to protect them from wind damage or loss

- take special care over the storage of materials that are potentially polluting (see Section 4.20)

- storage and use of perishable items (eg bags of cement) should follow the "first in first out" rule.

Handling

Handling of materials on site should be kept to a minimum to avoid the risk of damage and/or injury to site personnel. Materials should be handled using only the appropriate apparatus including cranes, trucks, fork lifts and even manual handling, ensuring that the suppliers' instructions on their operation are always followed.

Reuse of materials on site

Be aware of the potential to reuse existing materials on site, for example:

- valuable construction products that could be salvaged from existing buildings
- using excavated soils (this may be subject to a waste management licensing exemption) and other materials, on other areas of the site (eg for raising ground level or for general landscaping)
- reusing pallets delivered to the site in temporary works.

2.2.5 Traffic and access routes

It is important to manage site traffic because it can cause delays to local traffic and create a safety hazard both on and off site. People living and working near the site are also often annoyed by the emissions, noise and visual intrusion of queuing vehicles.

Access routes

The use of public roads for site access may be restricted in terms of:

- vehicle weight and width
- time restrictions
- parking
- minimising pedestrian conflict
- low-headroom (eg low bridge).

Consultation with the local police and local authority to address these issues and effectively manage them should occur before works begin. A traffic management plan should be devised and incorporated into the site management plan (see Section 3.6).

Managing site traffic

Plan the timing of deliveries to avoid vehicles waiting. Where several deliveries are likely to take place over a short period, designate a waiting area some distance from the site and call in deliveries when access is clear.

Arrange suitable designated car parking areas for site personnel to reduce the annoyance to the public. Consider implementing a park-and-ride or car-share scheme.

Construction sites are often blamed for disturbance caused by vehicles not associated with the site. To avoid this, give the main contractor and regular delivery vehicles visible identifying marks.

Checklist – Managing site traffic	
Develop a traffic management plan	
Designate an area of the site for site personnels' vehicles	
Put procedures in place to prevent delivery vehicles from queuing outside the site boundary	
Make delivery drivers aware of traffic restrictions on and around the site	
Delivery vehicle engines should be turned off while waiting to be unloaded	
Vehicles should be loaded and unloaded off the highway wherever possible	
Provide wheel washing facilities to avoid the spread of mud onto public highways	

2.2.6 Site clearance following completion

This is a phase of the works that usually receives little attention, but it can cause most problems. In clearing the site it is vital that wastes are managed in accordance with regulations (see Section 3.7), including avoiding burning of any clearance materials. Before a project is considered to be complete, the contractor is required to clear away, and remove from the site, all equipment and materials including:

- plant
- surplus materials
- waste and skips
- rubbish
- residues
- signage
- cabins
- temporary works.

2.3.1 Communication and community relations

Developing effective communication and consultation with the local community is important to minimise the likelihood of causing a nuisance (eg noise, dust, waste, etc), and should be initiated at the very start of the project and continued throughout. Techniques to do this include letter drops, newspaper articles and meetings.

If the community is aware of what is happening it is less likely to complain. Be prepared to explain the project and to answer questions. Do not deviate from the company or client commitments, or agree additional measures. Use it as an opportunity to listen and reassure.

Public consultation is particularly important when operations that cause disturbance are being carried out for a significant period of time. Try to explain the efforts that are being made to limit the impacts of operations by phasing and other control measures. Follow the steps in the checklist below when considering how to liaise with the local community.

Checklist – Liaising with local community (some points only appropriate to large sites)	
Identify key local community representatives, such as parish councillors, and keep them informed	
Visit occupants of sensitive buildings (such as schools, nursing homes and hospitals) and keep them informed of progress	
Prepare a leaflet and distribute it to nearby residents or occupiers. Provide updates or regular contributions to existing community newsletters	
Engage with the local community by working with local schools and charities	
Write articles about the progress on site for the local media	
Display a "contact board" at the site perimeter so that the public know whom to contact if they have a complaint or a comment to make. Use this board to display information on project phasing and other relevant matters	
Join a considerate contractor scheme	
Establish a complaint line and check that it works by calling it	
Deal quickly with any complaints that arise and in accordance with a defined complaints procedure. Create a log of complaints. Make sure all complaints are properly followed up and resolved	

Considerate contractor scheme

These schemes provide an ideal framework to demonstrate a project's environmental good practice intentions, but do not replace the need for an EMS (see Section 2.1.7). The local authority often administers them, although the national Considerate Constructors Scheme is also well-established. Registering the site with such a scheme gives the project additional points with environmental assessment methodologies such as CEEQUAL (Civil Engineering Environmental Quality and Assessment Award Scheme) and BREEAM (Building Research Establishment Environmental Assessment Method). Refer to their respective websites, www.ceequal.com and www.breeam.org, for further information.

For more information about the Considerate Constructors Scheme visit www.ccscheme.org.uk. Further details on the code of practice can be found on the accompanying CD.

Site personnel off-site

Good community relations can be quickly undone by the actions of the site personnel when off-site. Ensure that all personnel know what is expected of them. Causes of annoyance to the community can include:

- noise on arriving or leaving site
- too many site personnel in local shops and pubs,
- offensive language and behaviour
- vehicle parking.

Case Study

On a particularly controversial road construction site, the site manager used contact with local schools as one of the site's initiatives to keep the community informed about the scheme. A detailed information pack was prepared for each of the local schools to use as a teaching aid.

Good housekeeping

Good housekeeping is an important part of good environmental practice and it helps everyone to maintain a more efficient and safer site. The site should be tidy, secure, and have clear access routes that are well signposted. The appearance of a tidy, well-managed site can also reduce the likelihood of theft, vandalism or complaints.

Checklist – Good housekeeping	
Segregate different types of waste as it is produced and arrange frequent removal	
Keep the site tidy and clean – a tidy site is a safe site	
Ensure that no wind-blown litter or debris leaves sites	
Ensure that material and plant storage areas are properly managed. Cover lightweight materials with sheeting if necessary	
Keep hoardings tidy – repair and repaint when necessary removing any fly posting or graffiti	
Brush-clean the wheel washing facilities frequently	
Keep haul routes clean	
Keep roads free from mud by using a road sweeper	
Ensure site is secure	

Working hours

Site working hours can create considerable concern and annoyance among neighbours. On some projects, working hours for noisy operations are defined by the contract documents or by local authorities – perhaps through a Section 60 notice or 61 agreement (see Section 3.3). This route should be followed early in the project to reduce delays, by discussion with the local environmental health officer.

There may be opportunities for extending working hours in consultation with the local authority, but their effect on neighbours should be considered carefully – try to restrict working to sociable hours. When extended working is needed, it is important to inform neighbours in advance of the reasons for the work and its duration. Do not assume that the community's preference is for normal working hours as it may prefer longer working hours to reduce the overall length of time that they will be disrupted.

Time activities within the day carefully. For example, in the same way that it is advisable to schedule deliveries outside of rush hour, other intrusive activities can be scheduled at less sensitive times. To understand the constraints, which will vary from site to site, it is important to understand the daily patterns of the neighbours. Some points to consider include:

- in city centre sites night time noise may be more acceptable than daytime noise if there are no residential areas

- avoid noisy activities during school hours (particularly during exam periods)
- local restaurants appreciate less disturbance over lunch and dinner time
- whether local businesses require quieter periods during the day
- whether weekend or night time working is especially sensitive
- whether particularly sensitive areas (eg hospitals) are located near the site.

2.3.2 Lighting

Lighting can be an important deterrent to vandals and thieves, but it can also annoy the local residents. Keep any site lighting at the minimum brightness necessary for adequate security and safety. Locate and direct the lighting so that it does not intrude on nearby properties. Remember that high levels of lighting waste both energy and money. Consider using infra-red lighting for security. Be aware of the possible presence of bat roosts on site and position lighting accordingly to reduce impacts.

2.3.3 Site security

With many environmental offences being based on strict liability, with little or no defence available, contractors can be held liable for environmental damage even when it is caused by vandals.

Site security is an important component of good environmental management. Vandals often cause damage that harms the environment, by:

- opening taps on tanks containing fuel, or cutting fuel lines
- tipping out other liquids from drums and containers
- damaging/stealing raw materials
- playing on plant – damaging it and using it to cause damage
- spraying graffiti or flyposting on site hoardings
- destroying works in progress
- setting materials on fire.

Rural areas may also suffer from vandalism and especially theft, as their remote location provides time for thieves to remove plant and equipment without disturbance. The need for a manned presence in a remote location is often as important as in an urban setting.

Help to reduce vandalism by securing the site, and moving valuable items and those prone to theft from public view. Store these goods in a locked container or storage area.

A secure site helps ensure the safety of the community, particularly children, as construction sites are dangerous places in which to play.

Checklist – Suggested security measures	
Site boundary	
Secure the site boundary using perimeter fencing and high quality locks on gates. Solid barriers (eg hoardings) are more difficult to scale than chain link fences and prevent casual surveillance by prospective thieves	
Do not stack materials against the inside or outside of a site boundary/fence as this can provide an opportunity for vandals and thieves to scale it	
Within site	
Ensure that materials that are potentially hazardous are well-secured. It is a legal requirement to lock fuel outlets when they are not in use, and provide secondary containment for oil in storage	
Secure and immobilise plant and equipment overnight to prevent vandalism	
If the site is large or at high risk from trespassers Install deterrents such as lights, warning notices, 24-hour security guards, alarm systems and CCTV	
Monitor movement of people on and off site through the use of site passes or swipe cards	
Position the site manager's office to give a good view of the site	
Inform local police about the site and seek their advice on security	
Consult Fire Brigade for advise on storing fuel and flammable materials on site	
If the site experiences a problem such as vandalism or graffiti, ensure that appropriate clean-up/ repair is undertaken promptly, to discourage further problems from occurring	

Key Guidance

Dealing with vandalism – a guide to the control of vandalism, CIRIA SP91

2.4 Incident preparedness and response

The likelihood of an incident can be minimised by effective planning through development of a site pollution incident response plan. The plan needs to identify the on-site risks and appropriate responses. Suitable equipment, such as spill kits, oil booms and absorbent material, should be held at appropriate locations on site. An effective pollution incident response system relies on the following elements:

- effective pre-planning (eg use of drip-trays and booms)
- identification of contact numbers (see below)
- definition of site personnel responsibilities
- appropriate site personnel training
- dry-running of incident scenarios – spill drills
- availability of suitable spill kits at appropriate locations on the site.

Further details on incident preparedness can be found within the environment regulators Pollution Prevention Guidance note (PPG) 21 *Pollution incident response planning* (see Appendix 3).

Incident response plan

Ensure that all appropriate personnel are aware of the company's emergency procedure, that drain covers and spill kits are available, and personnel know how to use them. An incident response procedure (see Figure 2.4.1) should be based around the principle of:

STOP ⇨ **CONTAIN** ⇨ **NOTIFY** ⇨ **CLEAN UP**

Contact details that must be readily available:

- list of site personnel and sub-contractor offices
- your company's environmental representative
- fire-brigade/police – (999)
- environmental regulator – (0800 80 70 60)
- local authority environmental health department
- sewerage provider
- equipment suppliers (skip hire for waste disposal)
- liquid waste disposal contractors.

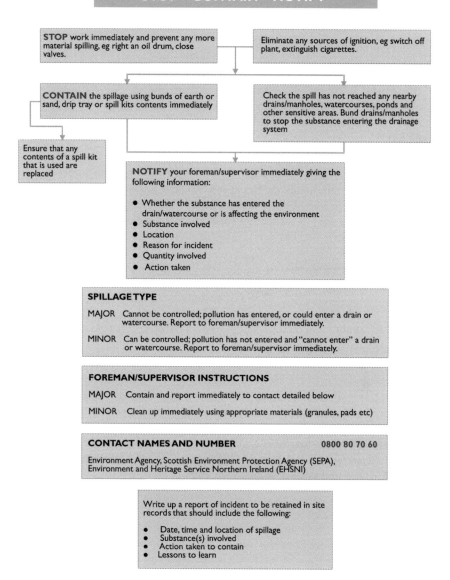

STOP – CONTAIN – NOTIFY

STOP work immediately and prevent any more material spilling, eg right an oil drum, close valves.

Eliminate any sources of ignition, eg switch off plant, extinguish cigarettes.

CONTAIN the spillage using bunds of earth or sand, drip tray or spill kits contents immediately

Check the spill has not reached any nearby drains/manholes, watercourses, ponds and other sensitive areas. Bund drains/manholes to stop the substance entering the drainage system

Ensure that any contents of a spill kit that is used are replaced

NOTIFY your foreman/supervisor immediately giving the following information:

- Whether the substance has entered the drain/watercourse or is affecting the environment
- Substance involved
- Location
- Reason for incident
- Quantity involved
- Action taken

SPILLAGE TYPE

MAJOR Cannot be controlled; pollution has entered, or could enter a drain or watercourse. Report to foreman/supervisor immediately.

MINOR Can be controlled; pollution has not entered and "cannot enter" a drain or watercourse. Report to foreman/supervisor immediately.

FOREMAN/SUPERVISOR INSTRUCTIONS

MAJOR Contain and report immediately to contact detailed below

MINOR Clean up immediately using appropriate materials (granules, pads etc)

CONTACT NAMES AND NUMBER   0800 80 70 60

Environment Agency, Scottish Environment Protection Agency (SEPA), Environment and Heritage Service Northern Ireland (EHSNI)

Write up a report of incident to be retained in site records that should include the following:

- Date, time and location of spillage
- Substance(s) involved
- Action taken to contain
- Lessons to learn

Figure 2.4.1: *Example incident response procedure*

Responsibilities

Make sure everyone knows who is responsible for:

- taking charge at the scene
- reporting to the site manager
- reporting to the appropriate environmental regulators
- recording events as an incident record
- regularly checking that contents of the spill kits are complete.

Spill kits

Spill kits, usually consisting of equipment to contain and absorb spills on land and water, are ideal for dealing with spillages. Obtain them from a reputable supplier and make sure they are specific to the oils and chemicals you have on site. You need to assess at the start of the project the number and deployment of kits for quick access across site. The contents of a spill kit will depend on the project, but are likely to include:

- oil-absorbent granules
- floating "booms" or "sausages"
- absorbent mats
- drain covers
- polythene sheeting and bags
- string
- gloves
- knives
- shovels.

Spill kits should be stored in a marked bag or wheely bin in a well-signposted location. It is best to store them near to where they may be needed. Ensure that, if materials from the spill kit are used, that these are replaced immediately. Once equipment from a spill kit has been used it will need to be disposed of carefully. Some equipment may be hazardous waste (special waste in Scotland) and must be disposed of in accordance with Duty of Care legislation and the **Hazardous Waste (England and Wales) Regulations 2005**.

Booms

If working close to a river, plan for emergencies by attaching the boom to a chain submerged across the river bed that can quickly be used to pull the boom into place in the event of a pollution incident. It is also important to note that booms need to be long enough to stretch over the river and be appropriate to the type of work being undertaken. On navigable rivers the navigation authority should be notified before the boom is installed.

Drip trays

Where drip trays are needed, these should be used with absorbent mats. Care should be taken to ensure that drip trays do not fill up with rainwater as this will render them useless.

Other equipment

There is also a wide range of proprietary equipment available from suppliers to deal with spillages. Special mats can be used to block drains or absorbent cushions located at the source of leaks or under pipe joints.

3.1 Archaeology and built heritage

Supplementary information can be found by referring to:

In this handbook	On accompanying CD
Construction process	
4.2, 4.7, 4.8, 4.9, 4.10, 4.12, 4.13, 4.15, 4.18	■ Environmental Archaeology. A guide to the theory and practice of methods, from sampling and recovery to post excavation, English Nature. Toolbox talks: 1, 4, 15

Why is protecting archaeology and built heritage important?

Archaeological remains and built heritage are an irreplaceable and valuable part of our national heritage. Buildings and structures – some that are only a few decades old – (or others that are hundreds of years old) are important assets of the built environment and need preserving. For this reason archaeology and built heritage are an important material consideration in the planning process.

Professional archaeologists may need to conduct on-site works to assess the nature and extent of remains so that an archaeological statement can be submitted in support of a planning application. They may be commissioned as a condition of planning permission either to supervise their protection during construction works or to excavate and record remains that are to be destroyed. Archaeological and heritage considerations should, therefore, be built into the project plan at the earliest opportunity to:

● ensure that remains to be preserved are protected by designing buildings that will not affect them, and during construction

● prevent disruptions to project programmes and costs

● enable architects to add value by incorporating elements of the site's heritage in the final development

● comply with legal requirements relating to scheduled monuments, listed buildings and the protection of the historic environment generally through planning legislation.

The perception that archaeology will be found and construction will be stopped is widespread but erroneous. Archaeological remains receive a range of designations and/or statutory protection. The most significant sites will be Scheduled Ancient Monuments; however, many are unscheduled but are still important. They are, according to various UK planning guidance notes, a material consideration in the planning process. Archaeological evaluation may be required, for example, in support of a planning application, or excavation as a condition of planning permission. Either way it needs to be planned and budgeted for long before budgets and programmes are finalised and an application is lodged, or opportunities will be missed and unexpected costs and delays will arise.

Sources of archaeological information

Depending on the project's nature and location, work may have been undertaken to investigate the archaeology of the site during the planning stage. Examples of this work are outlined here because it may be a useful source of information about the site. It is generally the client's responsibility to ensure that sufficient investigation has been undertaken to satisfy planning requirements (these are identified in local and national planning policies – see "Key Guidance" at the end of this section). However, this responsibility can transfer to the contractor in a design and build scheme.

Where important archaeological remains (whether they are scheduled or not) are affected by a proposed development, the emphasis is on preserving them. If preservation *in-situ* is not feasible, an archaeological excavation for the purposes of preservation by record may be an acceptable alternative.

When applying for planning permission, clients may be advised by the local planning authority to commission a desk-based archaeological assessment report as supporting documentation to the planning application. This report will review the archaeological potential of the site, assess the impact of the proposed scheme and propose a mitigation strategy.

If there is not enough information to decide how to proceed with the site, an evaluation may be proposed, which may involve the following:

- Phase I survey – desk study to identify sensitive areas on site which, aside from identifying archaeological remains, could lead to the identification of potential unexploded ordnance
- archaeological site investigation which may include trial pits/trenches (see Figure 3.1.1), geophysical surveys, boreholes/auguring, air photography and local history sources)
- Phase II survey – intrusive sampling.

Using all available information, including the results of any assessment and/or evaluation, the local planning authority will decide how the archaeological issues on that site should be managed: it may refuse or grant permission without condition, or may impose a planning obligation or condition on planning permission. It may issue a brief setting out what works are to be undertaken and then require a written scheme of investigation to be submitted for approval before works begin.

Figure 3.1.1: *Archaeological dig in progress at the Cambridge Grand Arcade*

As archaeological evaluations and excavations usually occur early in the project they may be specified in the contract, particularly where the contractor is to provide attendances for the archaeological work. Consideration should be given to the season in which archaeological works are undertaken, that is when is it most opportune.

Managing archaeology on site

If it is likely that archaeological or historical features will be found during a project, the client will probably have commissioned some work on the site. Ask the client for the information they hold about the site.

Even if an investigation has been carried out there may still be a potential for unexpected finds to be uncovered, particularly during earthworks and excavation (see Section 4.9 and 4.10). The contractor's responsibilities and liabilities will depend on the contract type and the site manager should be aware of the requirements.

The discovery of archaeology on site could lead to secondary impacts, such as the necessity to stockpile large quantities of material while further investigation is being carried out and the generation of dust and effects on site ecology (refer to Sections 3.2, 3.3 and 3.9 for further guidance).

Comply with any contract and planning conditions

Identify any contractual obligations and conditions that may be attached to the planning permission (see above).

Protect known archaeological or historical features

Ensure that the proposed method of working complies with any obligations identified. Works that are located close to a site of archaeological or cultural significance can have a damaging impact. For example, vibration or tunnelling could cause cracking and subsidence in listed buildings; access road traffic could disturb sensitive historic structures.

The levels of vibration that can cause damage to buildings vary considerably. It is always worth agreeing with the client the condition of susceptible buildings/monuments before works begin, and monitoring them thereafter. Seek specialist advice if vibration is likely to be a problem (see Section 3.5). Highlight the potential for significant effects on such buildings/monuments to site staff and identify control measures before starting work.

Dewatering works can cause draw-down of water and differential settlement, affecting archaeological materials that had been well preserved by being waterlogged. In such cases ensure that there is agreement on how to avoid or minimise such damage.

March

Opportunities to preserve remains *in-situ* can be incorporated into design work not only during the pre-construction planning stages but also when remains are revealed during construction. The Channel Tunnel Rail Link project preserved a number of sites including a Neolithic long barrow and a Roman temple.

The heritage bodies

- English Heritage, tel: 020 79873 3000
- Historic Scotland, tel: 0131 668 8600
- Environment and Heritage Service Northern Ireland, tel: 028 90251477
- Cadw (Welsh Historic Monuments), tel: 01443 336 000
- Institute of Field Archaeologists (lists Registered Archaeological Organisations, the QA scheme for archaeology), tel: 0118 378 6446
- Institute of Historic Building Conservation, tel: 01747 873 133.

The heritage bodies have a general duty to conserve heritage, schedule and undertake research etc. Unless dealing with Scheduled Ancient Monuments, contact the local planning authority archaeologist in the first instance for archaeological matters and the local authority conservation officer for listed buildings. The county/local authority/regional and island archaeologist has responsibility for planning issues.

Removal of human remains

Under the **Burials Act 1857** it is necessary to obtain a licence from the Home Office to disturb any human burials. The licence is normally issued with conditions regarding the removal and disposal of such remains by an archaeologist.

Under the **Disused Burial Grounds Act 1981** rather more stringent provisions relate to works affecting recognised cemeteries. A public notification procedure is involved as well as conditions being set down regarding the removal and disposal of human remains.

Treasure trove

Under the **Treasure Act 1996** (for England, Wales and Northern Ireland), certain finds are treasure, including:

1 Coins that are at least 300 years old.
2 Objects containing at least 10 per cent of gold or silver and at least 300 years old.
3 Any object that is found in the vicinity of known treasure.

Report all finds of treasure immediately to your local police station who will advise you on what to do next.

Listed buildings

The purpose of listing and protection given

In giving a building statutory protection against unauthorised demolition, alteration and extension, listing is an integral part of the system for managing change to our environment through the planning process administered by local planning authorities and the Office of the Deputy Prime Minister.

Planning authorities and National Park authorities have the power to serve a Building Preservation Notice (BPN) on the owner of a building which is not listed, but which they consider is of special architectural or historic interest and is in danger of demolition or alteration in such a way as to affect its character as a building of such interest.

A BPN provides protection to a building in that, for a period of six months after service of the BPN, it is subject to the same rules as if it were, in fact, listed – allowing time for a formal assessment to be carried out. The planning authority generally serves a BPN on the owner of the building and then requests that the building be considered for listing. The Secretary of State must decide within six months whether to list the building. If it is not listed, compensation may be payable if loss has been sustained as a result of the BPN.

Buildings of special architectural or historic interest

The Secretary of State for Culture, Media and Sport is responsible for compiling the statutory list of buildings of special architectural or historic interest. The heritage body is responsible for providing expert advice on which buildings meet the criteria for listing, and for administering the process.

The heritage body is responsible for considering and advising on all applications for listing, and for making recommendations to the Secretary of State about whether to add buildings to the statutory list. A building is assessed against the criteria published in Planning Policy Guidance 15 *Planning and the Historic Environment*. Before a full assessment is made, the owner and local authority will be informed that listing is being considered (unless the building is considered to be under immediate threat), and asked for comments.

If there is any doubt about the significance of the building, the heritage body may undertake historical and documentary research, and make comparisons with other examples of the same building type. In most cases an inspection will be undertaken, although this is not always necessary. Where the heritage body considers that an inspection is desirable, the owner's permission will be sought.

When the assessment is complete, and any comments from the owner and local authority considered, the recommendation will be forwarded to the Department for Culture, Media and Sport. Once a decision has been reached, the owner, applicant and local authority will be notified, and sent a letter detailing the reasons for the decision.

Further details on identifying historic monuments and protected sites are available from www.magic.gov.uk

Changes in listing

From 1 April 2005 new notification and consultation procedures for owners and local authorities were introduced, as well as clearer documentation for list entries. Further changes will be made, including the introduction of new information packs for owners. The intention is to make the heritage protection system simpler, more transparent, and easier for everyone to use.

Site checklists – Archaeology and built heritage	
Watching brief	
Be prepared for unexpected finds whether or not known archaeological or historical features have been identified on your site	
During excavations look out for burned or blackened material, brick or tile fragments, coins, pottery or bone fragments, skeletons, timber joists or post holes, brick or stone foundations, in-filled ditches	
If addressed at the right time and in the right way, finds may not necessarily affect the progress of the works	
If you are unsure about a find call in an archaeologist to assess it	
An archaeologist employed by the company may be able to agree suitable mitigation strategies by telephone with the planning authority archaeologist	
With the right advice delays may be much less than any statutory period	
If any unexpected finds are encountered	
Immediately stop work in the area	
Protect the find by fencing/blocking it off and contact the site manager	
Contact the local archaeological officer at the local authority	
Consider seeking specialist archaeological advice on how to proceed	
If human remains are discovered a Home Office licence will be required before works can continue	
Contractor responsibilities (though not expected to be an expert)	
Pursue the contractual obligations, eg providing attendances and/or access to professional archaeologists, sharing of H&S documentation	
Protect known archaeological and heritage sites	
Report any significant finds arising during construction	

3.1 Archaeology and built heritage

Legislation

A brief summary and interpretation of the legislation relevant to construction activities can be found free of charge on the Internet at www.netregs.org

Additionally, CIRIA has produced supporting good practice advice which is available free of charge at www.ciria.org/complianceplus

Removal of human remains

Under the **Burials Act 1857** it is necessary to obtain a licence from the Home Office to disturb any human burials.

Working on consecrated ground

The **Disused Burial Grounds Act 1981** sets stringent conditions regarding the removal and disposal of human remains.

Works to or around scheduled monuments

Require the prior consent of the Secretary of State via a Scheduled Monuments Consent. The consent protects any object or structure fixed to or around the building. Carrying out unauthorised works is a criminal offence for which significant penalties exist.

Working around listed buildings

A Building Preservation Notice (BPN) can be served by the planning authority on the owner of a building, which is not listed, but is considered to be of special architectural or historic interest.

Discovering treasure

Under the **Treasure Act 1996** (for England, Wales and Northern Ireland) all finds of treasure must be reported to your local police station immediately. This does not apply in Scotland where, under Scottish law, all ownerless objects belong to the Crown.

Working in areas of archaeological importance

Requires six weeks "operations notice" to the planning authority of any proposals to disturb the ground, tip on it or flood it.

Local authority powers

Local authorities are responsible for protecting a wide range of archaeological remains. Where development threatens to damage or destroy remains, the authority can require appropriate investigation through a planning condition or legal agreement. In certain circumstances it can also secure the positive long-term management of sites.

3.2 Buying, storing and managing materials

Supplementary information can be found by referring to:

In this handbook	On accompanying CD
Construction process	
4.3, 4.4, 4.6, 4.7, 4.8, 4.9, 4.11, 4.20	▪ Greenpeace Good Wood Guide ▪ WRAP Quality Protocol for the Production of Aggregates from Inert Waste Toolbox talks: 1, 4, 9, 13, 14, 15, 24

Important considerations when buying, storing and managing materials

Materials can be natural resources such as timber or from man-made sources such as cement. When buying materials from natural resources it is important to ensure they are from sustainable sources wherever possible, for example the buying of Forest Stewardship Council (FSC) certified timber. Storing materials correctly is vital to limit potential environmental impacts and reduce unnecessary damage or spoilage of materials, which could result in extra costs to the project.

Buying materials

When buying materials you need to consider their source. The three examples of material types offer guidance on material selection:

Preferred materials – for example sustainable timber certified by FSC

This list covers materials and substances that are considered to be preferable due to their reduced environmental impact. The inclusion of materials and substances does not imply that they have zero environmental impact, but their use represents a tangible step towards the protection of the environment and/or human health.

Advisory materials – for example solvent based paints

This list includes certain materials and substances, which are not banned by legislation, but should be avoided, as they are potentially hazardous or environmentally damaging in certain circumstances. Advice should be sought from your environmental manager if clarification is required.

Prohibited materials – for example asbestos

There are a number of materials and substances that are banned by UK or European law. These should not be used on site, nor should substances be substantially present in products supplied. National or local legislation may prohibit the use of other materials or substances on certain sites in specific circumstances.

CIRIA C650

For further information on buying materials refer to *The green guide to specification* (see "Key Guidance" at the end of the section) and for further examples of materials under each category on the accompanying CD.

Encouraging material resource efficiency

It is common practice that an extra 5–10 per cent of materials are ordered to allow for site wastage through damage, spillage, under-supply and vandalism. These figures should be reduced. The materials resource efficiency checklist can be used as a focus for looking at how materials are ordered, delivered, stored and handled on site to investigate how wastage can be reduced.

The choice of packaging through discussion with the materials supplier can assist the effective on-site storage and movement of materials. It can assist in the reuse of packaging items by segregating packaging for recovery and also assisting take-back of unused materials (eg plasterboard).

Key materials requiring careful consideration when used on site

Timber
Pressure for the industry to buy timber from sustainable sources has become more prevalent through a number of pressure groups including Friends of the Earth and Greenpeace who have 'named and shamed' specific construction projects for their use of non-sustainable timber. Guidance on buying sustainable timber can be found in the *Good Wood Guide* by Greenpeace (available on accompanying CD) and through membership of the World Wildlife Fund (WWF) 95+ Group.

Figure 3.2.1: *FSC certified timber – Bovis*

Timber certification is an important tool for providing evidence to stakeholders that timber is procured from legal and sustainable sources (see Figure 3.2.1). In response to an increasing demand for verifiable sustainable sources of timber, a number of credible certification systems have been developed, for example FSC,

Programme for Endorsement of Forest Certification (PEFC). Any timber used on site should have a certified chain of custody as a minimum.

Further guidance on purchasing timber from sustainable sources can be found from Friends of The Earth and Greenpeace.

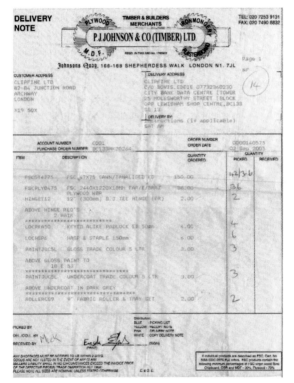

Figure 3.2.2: Above – *example delivery note and*
Above right – *chain of custody certificate – Bovis*

Aggregates

The use of recycled and secondary aggregates helps to reduce the demand for newly quarried materials and can be a cost effective alternative. Of the aggregates used in UK each year 50 million tonnes come from recycled or secondary sources. A good example is the use of pulverised fly ash (PFA) in cement to improve the quality, workability, water demand; used to increase strength and reduce rebars corrosion, but it does require longer curing. The use of PFA is well established, with manufacturers using up to the recommended maximum of 40 per cent to make their products.

The Aggregates Levy (AGL) tax was introduced in the UK on 1 April 2002. It is an environmental tax that is levied on the commercial exploitation of rock, sand and gravel when used as aggregate for construction purposes. The purposes of the levy are to maximise the use of recycled aggregate and alternatives to virgin aggregate, and to promote the efficient use of virgin aggregate. The AGL is, therefore, designed to encourage a shift in demand away from virgin aggregate towards recycled and alternative aggregates.

The importation, storage and placement of recycled material on site requires a waste management licence exemption at all times unless the material has been prepared substantively to the Waste and Resources Action Programme protocol – "Once a material has become a waste, it remains waste until incorporated into a product". The current fee for an exemption is £546.

Further information on specifying, purchasing or supplying recycled or secondary aggregates is available from the AggRegain website (www.aggregain.org.uk) developed by WRAP.

WRAP has also developed the quality protocol for the production of aggregates from inert waste regarding the use of secondary aggregates in construction. A copy of the protocol can be found on the accompanying CD with further details available from the AggRegain website.

Plasterboard

Plasterboard waste is often generated during renovation or demolition and should be stored under cover and away from moisture that could potentially damage the board by exposing it to mould. When disposing of plasterboard it should be classified as non-hazardous, non-inert waste and disposed of in a non-hazardous landfill site. Landfilling plasterboard waste is not encouraged as it has a high sulphur content, which can lead to odour problems. Construction projects should seek to recycle plasterboard wherever possible.

Gypsum

Gypsum wastes are often produced from plaster and plasterboard manufacture and its subsequent use. Gypsum and other high sulphate wastes are considered to be hazardous only if mixed with other hazardous substances and wastes.

If the waste is not hazardous it should be disposed of in a non-hazardous landfill site. If this waste contains more than 10 per cent sulphate per load it will have to be disposed of in a separate cell where there is no biodegradable waste. Should this waste contain less than 10 per cent sulphate it can be disposed of in a non-specific cell in the landfill.

Polyvinyl chloride (PVC)

The construction industry is one of the largest consumers of PVC, using it extensively in applications such as piping, cladding, wiring, flooring, windows and many others. It is estimated that the construction industry consumes in the region 500 000 tonnes per annum. The issues surrounding PVC are contentious because of the many substances used in PVC manufacture and, as such, its use on site should be limited.

Formaldehyde

Formaldehyde is most commonly used as a bonding material for composite boards such as medium density fibreboard (MDF) and plywood. Exposure to even low levels of formaldehyde through inhalation can cause irritation to the eyes, nose, throat, mucous membranes and skin. Unsealed chipboard, plywood, fire retardants and some furnishings have been found to yield measurable quantities of formaldehyde and are linked with "sick building syndrome". In addition, when boards such as MDF are cut, a fine dust is created which can be respired leading to possible exposure to free formaldehyde.

Materials selection is considered to have significant environmental impact on projects by both CEEQUAL and BREEAM.

Storing materials

The correct storage of materials is necessary to ensure they are:

- located away from sensitive receptors
- not at risk of theft or vandalism
- not spoiled through exposure to the elements
- easily accessible
- unlikely to be damaged.

For guidance on effective storage of materials on site refer to the materials storage checklist.

Managing materials

Different materials need to be managed in different ways according to their potential environmental impacts. For example, fuel needs to be stored in compliance with **Control of Pollution (Oil Storage) (England) Regulations 2001** and located away from any watercourses (see Section 3.8). Similar Regulations have been consulted upon by the Scottish Executive for application in Scotland though at the time of this document going to print Scottish Regulations remain to be enacted. These Regulations do not apply in Northern Ireland and Wales, but consideration should be taken to meet the requirements, as they are designed to prevent contamination of the water environment which would be an offence under other legislation.

Materials including adhesives and solvents that are potentially hazardous will have **COSHH (Control of Substances Hazardous to Health)** datasheets, which stipulate how the materials have to be stored, used and disposed of. Some materials are perishable, for example bags of cement, which therefore need to be stored under cover.

Defra has published a *Groundwater protection code: solvent use and storage* under the **Groundwater Regulations 1998**. Copies of this code of practice can be downloaded from the Defra website (www.defra.gov.uk/environment/water/ground/solvents/index.htm).

Landscaping

Materials such as uncontaminated spoil arising from site set-up (see Section 2.2) can be used to create a temporary bund or acoustic barrier whilst works are in progress. Where the bund or barrier is situated needs careful consideration.

Do not locate it near to watercourses, but ensure it acts as an adequate screen for local residents. Spoil will need to be carefully managed because it could become colonised by invasive plant species, pests and wildlife (see Section 3.9).

If it is likely that the spoil will be utilised on site for a long period it is always worth considering profiling and vegetating it, so it looks aesthetically pleasing, is stable and will not cause silting of nearby watercourses (see managing stockpiles checklist). Be aware of the potential for silting from rain run-off from both temporary and permanent soil bunds and have measures in place to deal with the silty material.

Case study

A developer minimised the environmental impact of its work to improve 160 hectares of contaminated land, by reusing 300 000 cubic metres of demolition rubble, saving up to £2.7 million. Topsoil for landscaping the site was manufactured on site using green waste and sewage sludge, rather than excavating soil from other places. As well as minimising waste and quarrying, the reuse of materials resulted in a quarter of a million fewer lorry journeys.

Mould

Where any mould is discovered, you should isolate the affected materials and if the infestation is large, quarantine the area. This prevents the spread of mould and protects people from its harmful effects. It is likely that porous materials affected will have to be removed, whereas cleaning of semi-porous materials may be possible. This must be carried out only by specialist contractors. Good practice in the storage of materials will prevent problems.

Checklist – Buying, storing and managing materials

Materials resource efficiency

When ordering avoid: ▪ Over-ordering ▪ Ordering inappropriate lengths ▪ Ordering for delivery at the wrong time	
When deliveries arrive on site avoid: ▪ Damage during unloading ▪ Delivery to inappropriate areas of site ▪ Delivery of damaged goods ▪ Accepting incorrect deliveries, specification or quantity	
When storing materials avoid: ▪ Exceeding their shelf life ▪ Damage or contamination from incorrect storage ▪ Loss, theft and vandalism	
When handling materials avoid: ▪ Damage or spillage through incorrect or repetitive handling ▪ Delivering the wrong materials to the workplace	

Checklist – Use of aggregates on site

Ensure suitability for use ▪ Make sure that materials do not contain contaminants and that pH levels are suitable for use where the site is located. This can be achieved by undertaking: ▪ A laboratory (UKAS accredited) analysis of contaminants present ▪ Leachate tests for the contaminants identified	
Consultation ▪ The environmental regulator has a remit to protect groundwater sources from contamination and must be consulted before any recycled materials are used in the ground ▪ The laboratory results should be forwarded to the local environmental regulator technical team for approval to ensure that local conditions do not prevent the use of such materials	

Checklist – Materials storage (general). Please note some of these points may be legal requirements. Check with your environmental regulator.	
Store all containers of materials, such as oils and paints, in a bunded area	
Clearly mark the area(s)	
Store materials in suitable containers that are labelled appropriately with fitted lids, taps and tops in good condition	
Put control measures in place and/or locate spill kits near to bulk stores and ensure they are accessible and fully stocked	
Store material so as to guard against breakage, vandalism or theft	
Protect stores against flood damage or inundation	
Store waste in a designated area and separate into different waste streams	
Ensure the waste storage area is in good condition and contained to prevent rainwater infiltration	
Stockpiles should not cause silty runoff	
Stockpiles should not be too steep and/or stored near drains or watercourses	
Store away from main site access roads	

Checklist – Managing stockpiles	
Store topsoil for reuse in piles less than 2 m high to prevent damage to the soil structure	
Segregate different grades of soil	
Position spoil and temporary stockpiles well away from watercourses and drainage systems	
Minimise movements of materials in stockpiles to reduce degradation of the soil structure	
Silty water formed by erosion of the stockpile must be managed correctly	
Direct surface water away from the stockpiles to prevent erosion at the bottom	
Place silt screens around spoil heaps to trap silt from any surface water run-off	
Vegetate long-term stockpiles to prevent dust in dry weather conditions, and reduce erosion of the stockpile to form silty runoff. Ensure adequate weed control	

Checklist – Refuelling protocol	
Designate a bunded refuelling area – preferably isolated from surface water drains. If not possible, install an oil separator in the surface water drainage system	
Avoid using remote fill points. Where these are unavoidable install suitable oil separators to the surface drainage system	
Avoid refuelling close to watercourses. Where this is unavoidable keep materials such as absorbent pads or booms readily available in case of spillage	
All refuelling must be supervised. Do not leave valves open unattended. (NB: auto-close valves may be a legal requirement)	
Keep an emergency spill kit at each refuelling point. If mobile refuelling is carried out, ensure each bowser carries a spill kit	
Bowsers should have an automatic cut out	
Ensure that personnel carrying out refuelling are aware of the protocol and know what actions to take in an emergency	

Checklist – Storing oils, fuels and chemicals	
Securely store all containers that contain potential pollutants (eg fuels, oils and chemicals) according to oil storage legislation	
Label containers clearly so that appropriate remedial action can be taken in the event of a spillage	
Regularly check taps and hoses for leakage	
Avoid storing drums tightly against each other. Store drums so that they can all be inspected for leaks	
Prevent damage from vandalism. Ensure that all valves and trigger guns are vandal and tamper proof	
Mark the contents of any tank clearly. Display a notice that demands that valves and trigger guns are locked when not in use	
Store tanks or drums in a secure bunded container or compound that is locked when not in use	
It may be particularly necessary to have an impermeable base where chemicals are stored in areas of groundwater risk. This should be identified in the contract but may be worth discussing with the environmental agencies	
Provide separate fill pipes for each tank unless the tanks are interconnected by a balance pipe of greater flow capacity than the fill pipe	
Mark fill pipes with the product type and a tank number where there is more than one tank	
Before moving a drum, check the bung is secure	

Checklist – Bunding tanks	
To avoid accidental spillage, bund tanks with a minimum capacity of 110% of the volume of the largest tank or 25% of the total storage capacity, whichever is the greater	
Do not allow bunded areas to fill with rainwater or slops (ideally, provide a cover). Empty any water collected in an appropriate way	
Site tanks away from vehicle movements and mark them clearly so that they are visible and so that people know they are a potential risk	
Do not put tanks where there is a direct link to surface drains, watercourses or sewers. Avoid placing tanks on unmade ground, to reduce the risk of soil contamination. Protect from vandalism	
The bund should be impermeable to the substance that is being stored in the tank	
Position air vent pipes so that they can be seen easily and directed so that any discharge (eg in the event of the tank being overfilled) is directed down into the bund	
Fill points should be inside the bund	
Fit any pumps sited outside the bund with a non-return/check valve installed in the feed line	

Key Guidance

PPG 2: and PPG 26 (See Appendix 3 on page 135 for details)

The Green Guide to Specification, 3rd Edition, BRE, Oxford Brookes University, Consignia, 2002

Managing materials and components on site, CIRIA Special Publication 146, 1998

A guide to the control of substances hazardous to health in construction, CIRIA R125

Storage of packaged dangerous substances, HS(G) 71, HSE, HMSO, 1992

The storage of flammable liquids in containers, HS(G)51, HSE, HMSO, 1990

Ground engineering spoil: good management practice, CIRIA R179

Legislation

A brief summary and interpretation of the legislation relevant to construction activities can be found free of charge on the Internet at www.netregs.org

Additionally, **CIRIA** has produced supporting good practice advice which is available free of charge at www.ciria.org/complianceplus

Storing hazardous materials

Under the **Control of Substances Hazardous to Health Regulations 2002 (COSHH)** materials that have properties such as explosive, flammable or toxic, etc, must be handled, stored and disposed of in accordance with the relevant COSHH datasheets.

Storing polluting materials

Under the **Control of Pollution (Oil Storage) (England) Regulations 2001** the storage of containers other than drums, requires the secondary containment to be of sufficient capacity to contain 110 per cent of the maximum contents of the container. Where more than one container is stored, the secondary containment should be capable of storing 110 per cent of the largest container or 25 per cent of the total storage capacity, whichever is the greater.

These regulations are applicable only in England. Similar regulations have been consulted upon by the Scottish Executive for application in Scotland though, at the time of this document going to print, Scottish Regulations remain to be enacted. These regulations do not apply in Northern Ireland and Wales, but consideration should be taken to meet the requirements, as they are designed to prevent contamination of the water environment which would be an offence under other legislation.

Stockpiling aggregate and other construction material

Under the **Waste Management Licensing (England and Wales) (Amendment and Related Provisions) (No. 3) Regulations 2005** a waste management licence exemption is required to stockpile aggregate and other construction material up to 90 cubic metres for a period of three months.

Equivalent regulations in Northern Ireland are the **Waste Management Licensing Regulations (Northern Ireland) 2003** and in Scotland are the **Waste Management Licensing Amendment (Scotland) Regulations 2004**.

Avoid causing a nuisance

Supplementary information can be found by referring to:

In this handbook	On accompanying CD
Construction process	
4.2, 4.4, 4.5, 4.7, 4.9, 4.10, 4.15, 4.16, 4.17, 4.18, 4.22, 4.23	Toolbox talks 1, 2, 3, 6, 8, 9, 17, 18, 21

Why is management of dust, emissions, and odours important?

Dust, emissions, and odours arising from a site may annoy neighbours and can cause air pollution. There is also the potential for legal action, which will have cost, programme and implications for reputation.

Dust is generally considered to be any airborne solid matter up to about 0.1 m in size. Particle sizes can vary considerably, depending on their origin, and the smallest particles can be breathed in. Some dust, such as limestone, is chemically active. Emissions from plant and generators can pollute the atmosphere and create unsavoury odours.

Annoyance to neighbours

Annoyance is caused when residents have to re-clean washing and when they have to wash cars, curtains and windows. Wind-blown dust can be unsightly over long distances in scenic areas. In exceptional circumstances dust can affect health by, for example, causing eye irritation. Asthma can be exacerbated by exposure to respirable dust.

Claims from farmers for dust damage to crops

Claims are particularly common on rural road projects. Even very low concentrations of dust can affect plant and fruit growth. Plant growth is especially susceptible to dusts that are highly alkaline, for example cement dust. Claims for damage to crops in excess of half a mile from the site have been made because dust can be blown for long distances.

Impact on project programme and budget

Some contracts may require that no work occurs at times of high wind in a certain direction. Working to comply with strict dust levels can impose cost and/or programme constraints. If a statutory nuisance is caused an abatement notice may be served by the local authority.

Impacts on ecology

Dust blowing onto watercourses can damage the ecology. As identified above, dust may also affect plant growth and alkaline dusts and light levels may change species composition in some situations. Ash trees may drop their leaves up to eight weeks early following exposure to high levels of dust.

Case Study

Tapley Pike is a Derbyshire heathland that has a soil pH of 3–4 and is dominated by plants that are adapted to relatively acidic environments. In some areas, due to limestone dust deposition, the soil was found to be 1.5 pH units higher (less acidic). This has resulted in domination by other species and several tree species may have died. Because of this change the numbers of animals and herbivorous insects have declined.

A company was fined £8500 under air pollution legislation for twice carrying dusty material in uncovered containers for a short distance on a public road.

How to avoid problems

Under the **Clean Air Act 1993** local authorities can impose limits on dust, emissions and odours generated from a site. Failure to keep within these limits can result in abatement notices being served when complaints have been received.

To avoid causing complaints, the site should adopt good working practices:

* identify sensitive receptors and inform the authorities of any likely nuisance that could occur and, as a good will gesture, agree to remedy the impacts
* put control measures in place to mitigate any negative impacts
* develop a daily monitoring regime to keep records of dust conditions. Your monitoring regime should note weather conditions, construction activities, their location and duration on site.

Dust suppression

It is essential to develop a strategy to stop dust being generated. Careful planning and design of construction operations can reduce dust eg speed limits on haul routes and locating stockpiles and batching plant in sheltered areas.

Damp down using water

Fine spraying of water (eg using a bowser as shown in Figure 3.3.1) is the most effective way to suppress dust. Repeat spray regularly, especially during warm and sunny weather when water will evaporate quickly. However, ensure that the application does not create excessive mud that can cause runoff into watercourses.

Figure 3.3.1: *Bowser dust control – Bovis*

Consider spraying:

- unpaved work areas subject to traffic or wind
- structures and buildings during demolition
- sand, spoil and aggregate stockpiles
- during loading and unloading of dust generating materials.

If you are abstracting water from a watercourse or fire hydrant, ensure that you have obtained the appropriate consent (see Section 3.8).

Damp down using water with chemical additives or binders

Damping down, using water in dry weather only, offers a temporary solution. For a more long-lasting solution it may be appropriate to mix additives and chemical binders to the water. Spraying with water and chemical additives is more effective than using water alone because it reduces the number of passes per day and the volume of water needed.

There is no general guidance as to which additive is best. The cost of the additives has to be weighed against savings in water supply, bowser usage and downtime. Take care to avoid over application which may cause pollution. Seek advice from the environmental regulator before using additives.

Dust screening

If dust-generating activities cannot be avoided, it may help to erect screens to act as windbreaks or as dust screens. These can take the form of permeable or semi-permeable fences, but be aware that they can be expensive if designed to resist high winds. Trees or shrubs planted early, as part of site landscaping, can provide some screening; likewise retention of existing vegetation (or buildings to be demolished) will aid screening.

Emissions and odours

Processes involving the use of fuels and the heating and drying of materials commonly emit fumes, odours or smoke. It is important to prevent emissions and odours as far as possible (refer to checklist at the end of the section). Any works that risk creating odours (eg works on sewers), should be phased carefully.

Dark smoke from plant and fires is a statutory nuisance. The local authority may serve notices to stop those activities generating the smoke.

Dust limits

If plant or machinery emits excessive (ie amounting to a nuisance) levels of exhaust emissions, local authorities have the power to prescribe limits on those emissions, the breaching of which may be an offence. Old plant, or plant carrying out an operation it is not designed for, is likely to fall foul of the prescribed limits.

Dust prediction and monitoring

There are a number of methods for monitoring dust on site and include:

1 Exposing microscope slides, sticky pads, or sticky covers to determine dust direction for a given period and calculating the deposition rate of dust over the exposed period.

2 Using high volume samplers to draw air through a filter to measure the volume of dust in the air at the time. Take samples before work starts to determine background levels, and compare these against those taken during construction.

3 The dry Frisbee dust deposit gauge (shown in Figure 3.3.2) uses a bowl and bottle to collect large and small dust particles. It should be situated 5 m away from any obstruction and left in place for a month before being replaced by a new one. After a month the bowl and bottle are removed, sealed, labelled with site location and date, then sent to the laboratory for analysis.

None of the methods provides definitive evidence of the dust impact and they can be costly. It may be useful for a contractor to volunteer to monitor dust as a demonstration of its commitment to good practice. This, in some cases, can be useful evidence in defence of a nuisance claim. It is often a contract requirement to monitor dust or emissions. Check this before you start work.

For a dust monitoring programme to give more definitive evidence of construction impacts it should include both upwind and downwind monitoring of the site and cover a baseline period before construction started. The baseline period should ideally cover the same seasons as the construction period. This level of monitoring is not generally recommended unless required by the contract or if the impact of dust is expected to be significant.

Figure 3.3.2: Dry frisbee dust deposit gauge – Morrison

Checklist – Dust, emissions and odours: avoid causing a nuisance	
Avoiding dust generation	
Haul routes	
Select suitable haul routes away from sensitive receptors if possible. Reduce the length and width of haul roads (while still allowing two way traffic) to minimise surface area from which dust may be produced	
Pave heavily used areas, or use geotextiles (eg around batching plant or haul routes). Sweep these regularly	
Sweep public roads regularly, using a vacuum sweeper	
Limit vehicle speeds – the slower the vehicles the less the dust generation	
Damp down	
Demolition	
Use enclosed chutes for dropping demolition materials that have the potential to cause dust. Regularly dampen the chutes	
Consent, under EPA 1990, is required for the use of mobile plant for crushing materials such as bricks, tiles and concrete	
Locate crushing plant away from sensitive receptors	
Do not use drills that are powered by compressed air as these generate large amounts of dust	
Plant and vehicles	
Clean the wheels of vehicles leaving the site so that mud is not spread on to the highways	
Ensure that exhaust fumes are directed upwards and not directly at the ground. Retractable sheeted covers on vehicles must be used to enclose dust	
Ensure all plant and vehicles are in good working order with an up-to-date maintenance log	
Vehicles must keep to site speed limits to reduce the risk of dust clouds	
Materials handling and storage	
Locate stockpiles out of the wind (or provide wind breaks) to minimise the potential for dust generation	
Keep the stockpiles to the minimum practicable height and use gentle slopes	
Compact and bind stockpile surfaces (in extreme cases). Revegetate long-term stockpiles	

Checklist – Dust, emissions and odours: avoid causing a nuisance (continued)	
Minimise the storage time of materials on site	
Store materials away from the site boundary, main site access roads and downwind of sensitive receptors	
Ensure all waste skips are enclosed or covered by tarpaulin	
Minimise the height of fall of materials	
Damp down earthworks during dry weather	
Concrete batching	
Mix large quantities of concrete or bentonite slurries in enclosed areas to avoid generating dust	
Cutting/grinding/grouting/packing	
Minimise cutting and grinding on site where possible	
On cutters and saws, use equipment and techniques such as dust extractors to minimise dust. Consider a wet cutting saw or use vacuum extraction or block splitters	
Spray water during cutting of paving slabs to minimise dust	

Preventing emissions and odours	
Vehicles and plant	
Keep vehicles and plant used on site well maintained and regularly serviced. Ensure that all vehicles used by contractors comply with MOT emissions standards at all times	
Control deliveries to site to minimise queuing	
Make sure that engines are switched off when they are not in use	
Keep refuelling areas away from the public	
No fires on site	
The only known exception to this is the burning of Japanese Knotweed with consent	
Waste storage	
To avoid odours use covered containers for organic waste (eg weeds and other vegetation) and remove frequently	
Chemicals on site	
To avoid odours: • Take account of the wind conditions when arranging activities that are likely to emit aerosols, fumes, odours and smoke • Position site toilets away from residential areas	

Legislation

A brief summary and interpretation of the legislation relevant to construction activities can be found free of charge on the Internet at www.netregs.org

Additionally **CIRIA** has produced supporting good practice advice which is available free of charge at www.ciria.org/complianceplus

Work activities that create dust, emissions and odours

Under the **Clean Air Act 1993** it is an offence to permit the emission of dark smoke from industrial or trade premises, which is generally enforced by local authorities. However, there are exemptions allowing emissions from the burning of timber and most other waste.

Your work activities can be a statutory nuisance

Under Part III of the **Environmental Protection Act 1990** dust, emissions and odours can be classified as a statutory nuisance. The local authority can serve an abatement notice on the person responsible (in practice the contractor) to put a stop to a statutory nuisance. Breaching an abatement notice is a criminal offence.

3.4 Ground contamination

Supplementary information can be found by referring to:

In this handbook	On accompanying CD
Construction process	
4.7, 4.9, 4.10, 4.18, 4.20	Toolbox talks 1, 9, 10, 11, 12, 13, 15, 18, 23

Why is managing ground contamination important?

Ground contamination often is present as a result of previous land use, for example industrial processes or landfill. If contamination is likely to be encountered the contract should define the methods of dealing with it. The contract will usually refer to the guidance on how to deal with contamination issued by statutory authorities. This section advises on how to deal with contamination (both expected and unexpected), and how to avoid causing or spreading contamination. Ground contamination may result in the following problems:

- delays to the programme through unexpected or accidental contamination

- liability for costs arising from unexpected spreading or making existing contamination worse and for disposal and/or remediation of contamination

- pollution of groundwater and surface watercourses

- pollution of surrounding land

- impacts on flora and fauna

- public concern and anxiety.

A major housebuilder and two other defendants were ordered by the Crown Court to clear 270 lorry-loads of waste containing hydrocarbons that had been dug out from a redundant gasholder and illegally dumped on farmland. The defendants were told that the level of fine would depend upon the clean up achieved.

The source-pathway-receptor model

An important consideration when dealing with contamination on site is the relationship between the source of the contaminant (eg underground oil storage tank), the pathway along which the contaminant can migrate away from site (eg groundwater) and the receptor (eg aquifer). This is the basis of the source-pathway-receptor model as illustrated Figure 3.4.1.

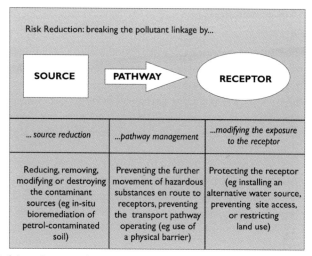

Figure 3.4.1: *Source-pathway-receptor model*

Contamination identified on site does not necessarily pose a threat on site or to those areas surrounding the site if it is left undisturbed. Work activities can mobilise contaminants (eg excavation puncturing a protective barrier), which can cause a pollution incident away from the site.

On some sites the best option is to leave the contaminants *in-situ* and/or encapsulate them. If this is the decided management option, the site documentation must record the precise location and extent of the contaminants to prevent disturbance.

How problems may arise

The problems associated with the discovery of contaminants on site can be successfully managed but, if they are not, they can cause problems by spreading the contaminants across or off the site. Activities that can lead to this occurring include:

- wind-blown contaminated dust arising from loading of lorries or trains
- stockpiling contaminated material on clean ground during works
- spillages of contaminants such as oil onto the ground during works
- dewatering of excavations that draws in contaminated groundwater from adjacent sites
- discharge of contaminated dewatering water into nearby watercourses.

3.4 Ground contamination

Getting to know your site

Responsibilities

It is the responsibility of the client to conduct good quality site investigations to determine the potential for contamination on site. Often the client will sub-contract this out to a suitably-qualified and experienced consultant. The results will be used to carry out a risk assessment based on the *Model procedures for the management of land contamination* (CLR 11) framework, and development of remedial plans that must be agreed by the planning authority before any work begins.

Contractor have a duty to ensure they are given all the background information regarding the sites and that they understand the history of the sites and the actions they have to take to fulfil the requirements of the remedial plan.

Preliminary investigation

The remedial plan to deal with any contamination found on site should be derived from a tiered risk assessment approach in accordance with CLR 11, which includes the following stages of data gathering:

- history of the site (details of its owners, occupiers and users)
- processes used (including their locations, raw materials, products, waste residues and methods of disposal)
- layout of the site above and below ground at each stage of development (including roadways, storage areas and other hard cover areas)
- presence of waste disposal tips, made ground, abandoned pits and quarries with or without standing water
- mining history (including shafts and roadways)
- information on geology and hydrogeology (including the presence of groundwater and surface water)
- potential contamination uses of sites, past or present, in the area adjacent to the site.

Site characterisation

If the preliminary investigation finds that contamination is probable, an exploratory investigation would be undertaken by the client to define:

- the type
- concentration
- extent of any contamination on the site.

Although a robust site characterisation reduces the likelihood of discovering unexpected contamination during site works, it is always possible. Method statements should always include the possibility of finding contamination and the mechanisms for dealing with it. Therefore, site personal (especially excavator operators) should be vigilant during excavations (see visual signs checklist at the end of the section).

> **Case study**
>
> A JCB operator was excavating a pipeline in the vicinity of a waste dump. During excavation, a soil slip resulted in part of the dump being exposed, including a number of drums. The JCB operator endeavoured to replace a slipped drum on the dump and in so doing pierced it. Exposure to the sun had caused it to expand and so the drum exploded, releasing an unknown gas. The driver was exposed to the vapours released from the drum and had to receive medical attention.

What to do if unexpected contamination is encountered

As mentioned above, the contractor should already have adopted appropriate working methods to deal with contamination that is expected. These will be detailed in the risk assessment. The following section deals with unexpected contamination.

During boring, digging, excavating and similar operations observe the uncovered ground and watch out for visual signs (refer to checklist) of contamination. The release of noxious fumes, petrol, oils, solvents, chemical residues and smells, may also indicate contamination. For example a smell of rotten eggs may mean that hydrogen sulphide contamination is present.

3.4 Ground contamination

When contamination is suspected do the following:

1. Stop work immediately.
2. Report the discovery to the site manager who must seek expert advice.
3. Seal off the area to contain spread of contaminants.
4. Clear site to ensure there is nothing that could cause fire or explosion.
5. Contact the regulator or local authority once it is confirmed that contamination is found.
6. Ensure that the suspected contamination is tested and characterised and agree changes to the existing remedial plan.
7. Follow good practice guidance to remediate the land.

Testing and analysis

Testing and analysis should be carried out on spoil and other materials when you are unsure whether it is contaminated. Sampling should be carried in accordance with best practice by competent specialists. Samples taken should be sent to a UKAS (United Kingdom Accreditation Services) accredited laboratory for testing against a suite of contaminants and its leachability. The results of the testing will determine if the materials are contaminated and therefore need appropriate disposal, or if it is uncontaminated and can therefore be reused on site or sent to an exempt site.

Chemical testing of soils carried out using the Monitoring Certification Scheme (MCERTS) performance standard provides assurances on the reliability of data from such tests. The performance standard is an application of ISO 17025:2000 specifically for the chemical testing of soil and covers:

- the selection and validation of methods
- sampling pre-treatment and preparation
- the estimation of measurement uncertainty
- participation in proficiency testing schemes
- the reporting of results and information.

Remediating contaminated land

There are various options available for dealing with contaminated land once it has been identified on site. The majority of remedial techniques to be carried out on site require an appropriate waste management licence. These options can be divided into:

CIRIA C650

Containment

This can involve the excavation and disposal of the contaminated material; physical containment through covers, barriers or liners; or chemical stabilisation

Separation

Physical separation of contaminants from the rest of the soil through soil washing, solvent extraction or particle separation.

Destruction

Physical destruction of contaminants through incineration; chemically through chlorination; biologically through the introduction of micro-organisms into the soil or through phytoremediation (use of plants).

These options should be considered on a site-by-site basis and the best practicable environmental option will be stipulated in the remedial plan. The above options can be divided into a number of techniques, summarised in Figure 3.4.2 below:

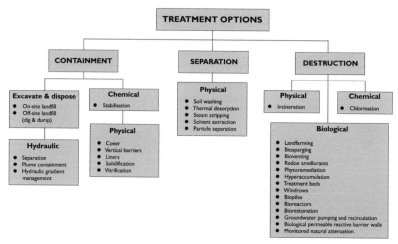

Figure 3.4.2:   *Remedial options*

Unexploded ordnance

The discovery of unexploded ordnance on site is unusual, and only likely to occur in areas of historic weapons manufacture or storage during the world wars. They may also be discovered in areas that received heavy bombardment during the Second World War such as London, Liverpool and Coventry, where it is most likely that unexploded ordnance may be found. If unexploded ordnance is suspected or found on site:

- stop work immediately
- clear the area
- contact police and army bomb disposal unit.

Checklist – Ground contamination	
Getting to know your site and remedial plans	
Carry out a preliminary investigation of site using a tiered risk assessment approach as set out in Model procedures for the management of land contamination (CLR 11)	
Undertake an exploratory investigation of the site to characterise contamination on site in terms of: ▪ type ▪ concentration ▪ extent	
Develop remedial plan from results of preliminary and exploratory investigations	
Agree remedial plan with local planning authority and make available to contractor	
Ensure relevant permits are in place for any remedial works required	
Avoid causing or spreading contamination	
Do not stockpile contaminated soil unless it cannot be avoided. If it is necessary, stockpile only on a hardstanding area to prevent contamination of underlying ground	
Cover stockpiled material to prevent wind-blown dust (potentially contaminated) and to prevent ingress of rainwater	
Control surface drainage from stockpiled area. Water draining from a stockpile may be contaminated and need controlled off-site disposal	
Be careful when handling, storing and using oils and chemicals	

Checklist – Ground contamination (continued)	
Visual signs	
Discoloured soil (eg chemical residues)	
Unexpected odours (eg hydrocarbons)	
Fibrous texture to the soil (eg asbestos)	
Presence of foreign objects (eg chemical/oil containers/waste)	
Evidence of previous soil workings	
Evidence of underground structures and tanks	
Existence of waste pits	
Artificial ground where the level has been raised by man's activities and not due to a natural cause, eg slag heaps	
Old drain runs and contamination within buildings – tanks, flues etc	
Topsoil adjacent to motorways can be contaminated by particulate deposition	

Key guidance

Regulatory

Framework for the classification of contaminated soil as hazardous waste, Environment Agency, 2004

HSG66 *Protection of workers and the general public during the development of contaminated land.* HSE.

Other

Model procedures for the management of contaminated land, Defra and Environment Agency (CLR 11)

BS 10175: 2000 *Investigation of potentially contaminated sites – Code of practice*

A guide for safe working on contaminated sites, CIRIA R132

Selection of remedial treatments for contaminated land. A guide to good practice, CIRIA C622

Contaminated land risk assessment. A guide to good practice, CIRIA C552

Ground engineering spoil: good management practice, CIRIA R179

For details of other relevant contaminated land guidance visit www.contaminated-land.org

3.4 Ground contamination

Legislation

A brief summary and interpretation of the legislation relevant to construction activities can be found free of charge on the Internet at www.netregs.org

Additionally **CIRIA** has produced supporting good practice advice which is available free of charge at www.ciria.org/complianceplus

Town and Country Planning Act 1990

Under this Act the local authorities are responsible for ensuring that land contamination is dealt with through the planning system and that remediation takes place where it is required. It is the responsibility of the **developer** to carry out the remediation and satisfy the local authority that the remediation has been carried out as agreed. Government guidance to planners *Planning policy statement 23 Planning and pollution control* advises that remediation is undertaken to ensure sites do not fall under Part IIA of the **Environmental Protection Act 1990** when completed.

Environmental Protection Act 1990 (Part IIA)

The key considerations under this Act are:

- possibility of causing significant harm to human beings, ecosystems and buildings, and the potential of polluting controlled waters
- polluter pays principle for the allocation of liability.

Risk assessment and risk management are fundamental to the approach adopted on remediation of contaminated sites. The risk assessment process comprises the following elements:

- the establishment of a linkage between the contaminant source, the migratory pathway, and the potential of significant harm on sensitive targets
- the determination of "significant harm" and "significant possibility of significant harm".

Waste Management Licensing (England and Wales) (Amendment and Related Provisions) (No. 3) Regulations

Under these regulations a licence is required to use a remedial technique on site. Equivalent regulations in Northern Ireland are the **Waste Management Licensing Regulations (Northern Ireland) 2003** and in Scotland are the **Waste Management Licensing Amendment (Scotland) Regulations 2004.**

The need to control it

Supplementary information can be found by referring to:

In this handbook	On accompanying CD
Construction process	
4.2, 4.4, 4.6, 4.7, 4.9, 4.10, 4.12, 4.13, 4.17, 4.18, 4.19	Toolbox talks: 4, 7, 15, 21

Why is noise management important?

Excessive noise on site not only represents a major hazard to site workers but can annoy neighbours and in some cases disturb adjacent wildlife.

March

Excessive noise is the single most common source of complaint against the construction industry, and can result in work being stopped on site.

Excessive noise and vibration can cause the following:

- poor quality of life for affected residents (ie disturbance and stress)
- complaints
- structural damage to buildings and utilities
- wildlife disturbance.

And lead to:

- statutory enforcement of controls by the local authority or court, including revisions to working methods, working hours and even stopping the works
- programme delays and associated costs
- damage to third party and community relations
- damage to corporate/project reputation
- damage to wildlife habitats.

Effective planning, and on-site management of noise, will significantly reduce the likelihood of any of these actions being taken, and so reduce the risk of construction noise affecting the overall performance of a project.

Understanding, adopting, communicating and integrating the legal requirement to employ best practicable means (BPM) to minimise noise and vibration at all times and all locations, is the best way to indicate to the local authorities, local residents and construction personnel that noise and vibration is being managed satisfactorily on site.

What is noise?

Noise is commonly referred to as unwanted sound. Sound is a wave transmitted as small changes in air pressure (known as sound pressure) between a source and receiver (ie a construction site and a nearby resident).

Noise units

The unit generally used for measuring or predicting construction noise was the L-weighted sound pressure level in decibels, denoted dB(A) as it combined the ease of measurement with a reasonable correlation with the average person's annoyance. But, it gave a measure of the overall noise the an instant it was measured only, and not an indication of the different frequencies within the noise. The unit now used by the industry is L_A, the types of L_A units commonly used are:

L_{Aeq} is a noise level measured in dB(A), which has been averaged over a specified time (eg 5 minutes, 1 hour or 24 hours). The L_{Aeq} is being used more frequently to describe noise that varies with time, and can be effectively used on a construction site where the noise level may vary continuously.

L_{A90} is the noise level that is exceeded for 90 per cent of the time during the measurement period, and is usually used as a measure of the background noise.

L_{Amax} is the maximum noise reached during the monitoring period, and is used to obtain instantaneous noise levels, which are used to calculate the L_{Aeq} and L_{A90}.

Certain activities, such as breaking out of concrete using a pneumatic breaker, have an impulsive noise character which, when evaluated over a longer-term (ie a working day), may not truly reflect the level of disturbance caused. For such activities L_{Amax} over a given period would better reflect the disturbance caused from such an activity, rather than using the L_{Aeq}.

Propagation

The level of noise observed from a construction activity at a nearby building is dependant on a number of factors, some of which can be controlled on site while others are dependant upon local conditions. To manage noise on site, consideration should be given to those factors which can be controlled, namely:

- the noise level of the activity (determined by construction method and plant selection
- level of screening between the noise source and the receiver point
- location of the activity within the construction site (if possible).

Local conditions which cannot normally be controlled on site are:

- distance from the noise source to the building
- reflections from adjacent buildings
- ground absorption
- atmospheric conditions (ie wind direction, humidity and temperature).

Effective planning

Careful planning of the construction works to take all reasonable and practicable steps to minimise noise and vibration, can significantly reduce the amount of disturbance and reduce the risk of noise abatement action. The best approach is to ensure that the legal requirement to employ BPM is understood by all staff and is integrated into the planning of all activities at all locations and at all times.

Best practicable means (BPM)

BPM as defined within **Section 72 of CoPA 1974** states that:

(1) *This section shall apply for the construction of references in this Part of the Act to best practicable means.*

(2) *In that expression "practicable" means reasonably practicable having regard among other thing to the local conditions and circumstances, to the current state of technical knowledge and to the financial implications.*

(3) *The means to be employed include the design, installation, maintenance and manner and periods of operation of plant and machinery, and the design, construction and maintenance of buildings and acoustic structures.*

(4) *The test of test practicable means is to apply only so far is compatible with any duty imposed by law, and in particular is to apply to statutory undertakers only so far as compatible with the duties imposed upon them in their capacity of statutory under-takers.*

(5) *The said test is to apply only so far as compatible with the safety and safe working conditions, and with the exigencies of any emergency or unforeseen circumstances.*

(6) *Subject to the preceding provisions of this section, regard shall be had, in construing references to "best practicable means", to any relevant provision of a code of practice approved under the preceding section."*

3.5 Noise and vibration

This is interpreted as the balancing of noise and vibration mitigation against:

- cost (clause 2)
- engineering practicability (clause 3)
- current state of technical knowledge/techniques (clause 2)
- duration (clause 3)
- proximity of the works to residents (clause 2)
- number of resident affected (clause 2)
- time of day (clause 3)
- safety (clause 5).

As BPM is a balancing of factors. It means that noise mitigation or working constraints can be prioritised to those locations and activities, which are most required. For example:

- proximity of works to residents – the further away from residents works occur the less mitigation is required to demonstrate BPM (eg 500 m away opposed to only 50 m)
- duration – if an activity is required to be undertaken only for a few days, then it would require significantly less mitigation than if it was to be undertaken for several weeks
- time of day – works undertaken at night require more mitigation and justification than works during the day
- engineering practicability and safety – if there is no alternative but to undertake the works at night with noisy equipment (because there is no quieter equipment that exists to do the work) then this would constitute BPM, as long as detailed justification was given and local residents were informed in advance of the works.

The following generic measures should be considered in the pursuance of BPM, in order of priority:

- control of noise at source:
  - selection of low noise methods
  - control of working hours
  - selection of quiet or low noise equipment
  - location of equipment on site
  - provision of acoustic enclosures.

- screening
  - local screening of plant
  - site perimeter hoarding.

If noisy activities have to be undertaken near residents over long periods then consideration can be given under BPM to provide protection. For example sound insulation to windows and ventilation at properties or temporary relocation of residents as a last resort. These approaches will be considered as BPM in law only if it can be demonstrated that all other forms of BPM noise control at source have been exhausted.

Control of noise at source

Selection of low noise methods

The best way to minimise the possible disturbance to residents is to minimise the amount of noise generated in the first place, ideally by selection of low noise generating methods. Some of the construction activities that cause the greatest problems are:

- piling (particularly by diesel hammer)
- breaking out with pneumatic tools
- scabbling of concrete
- falling ball demolition
- grit-blasting
- hydro-demolition.

These methods should be used only when all other practicable methods have been investigated and discounted or that their use minimises other environmental impacts. For example, hydro-demolition is very noisy but the level of dust produced in comparison to conventional demolition methods is significantly less. Therefore in certain situations it may be preferable to prioritise the control of dust rather than noise.

Working hours

The level of disturbance resulting from noise associated with a construction site activity is dependent on when and where the noise occurs. In residential areas people are more sensitive to noise in the evening, at night, at the weekend or on a bank holiday, compared to the normal working week. Therefore, wherever possible works should be limited to weekday daytime only.

In certain industrial/office areas, where the nearby properties are unoccupied during the evening and at the weekend, it may be better to programme noisy activities for during these periods.

For mixed residential and office buildings consider "quiet periods" during the daytime when certain noisy activities (eg piling) are not undertaken to minimise the effect on the office buildings. To balance the loss of daytime hours, work into the early evening or begin works earlier.

To limit the impact of a project on the local community, the local authority will stipulate the hours during which noisy works are allowed or it may restrict working hours by placing a limit on the average noise allowed over a given period (see section: prior consent below). In these cases, if the noise exceeds the limit set, the working period must be reduced or an alternative and quieter work method adopted.

BS 5228 – *Noise control on construction and open sites* describes the detailed calculations needed to work out the noise levels caused by a particular project. Further guidance is given in CIRIA Project Report 70, *How much noise do you make?* (1998).

Selection of quiet or low noise equipment

For many construction activities there are several items of plant which could be utilised to undertake a particular task, eg use of hydraulic jack method over impact drop hammer. In some circumstances the use of a single larger item of equipment rather than a number of small items of equipment can reduce noise levels on site, eg use of a single generator opposed to several smaller generators.

Provision of acoustic enclosures

Some equipment can be supplied with acoustic enclosures, such as hoods and doors on compressors and generators, or other noise control devices such as jackets on pneumatic drills and shrouds on piling rigs and cranes. These devices should not only be closed but also be tight fitting and well sealed. A partly closed door is of little use.

Screening

If designed and used correctly, screening can reduce noise levels from a site considerably at relatively low cost. Screening can be provided by existing buildings, earth bunds, site material storage, site security hoarding, or purpose built noise screens.

To screen a receiver from a noise source, there must be no "line of sight" between the source and the receiver. The amount of noise reduction provided by screening is dependant upon two factors:

1   The increase in distance between a noise source and receiver over (or around) a noise screen compared to the direct distance path, (known as path difference) which can be expressed as path difference = (distance A + distance B) – distance C.

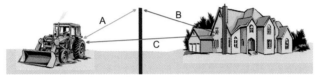

The following examples indicate where to place a noise screen to achieve the greatest noise reduction.

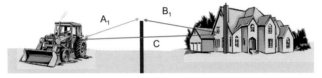

NOISE SCREEN 1: *Midway between source and receiver*

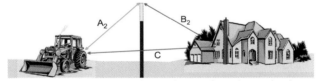

NOISE SCREEN 2: *Same as Noise Screen 1 but with the barrier height increased*

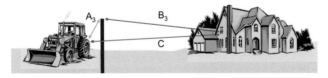

NOISE SCREEN 3: *Same as Noise Screen 1 but closer to the noise source*

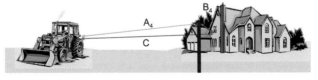

NOISE SCREEN 4: *Same as Noise Screen 1 but closer to the nearby residence*

2   Noise screens 3 and 4 provide the best level of noise reduction as they are close to either the source or thr receptor. Because the height of the barrier is lower there is a cost saving compared to screens 1 and 2. Therefore screens 3 and 4 are the most efficient in achieving BPM.

The amount of sound passing through the noise screen is controlled by:

a   density of the screen material (generally the higher the density the lower the level of sound passing through the barrier)

b   any holes/openings within the noise screen.

Generally the maximum reduction in noise level by a purpose-built screen or site security hoarding is 10 dB(A). This can be achieved by the provision of a screen that breaks the line of sight between the source(s) and receiver, and should be constructed from a material of density 7 kg/m^2 or higher such as:

- 12 mm (minimum) plywood
- 12 mm (minimum) chipboard
- 7 mm Plexiglas.

When there are no foundations upon which to construct a screen you can mount 12 mm plywood board from a frame supported by concrete "jersey" blocks.

Any gaps in the screen will significantly reduce the performance in reducing noise. It is common to construct the screen from two sheets of 12 mm board which should be overlapped to ensure that there are minimal gaps between the sheets. If a single sheet is to be used then careful sealing of the abutting sheets is required. The gap between the layers of a double-sheeted screen can be filled with a sound-absorbing material, such as mineral wool quilt, to prevent the build-up of reverberant sound.

Specific BPM measures to minimise noise and vibration

Specific mitigation measures, which should adopted where appropriate to demonstrate BPM, are:

- careful selection of equipment, construction methods and programming with the objective of reducing noise and vibration wherever possible. Only equipment, including road vehicles, conforming to relevant national or international standards, directives and recommendations on noise and vibration emissions, should be used.

- use of noise-control equipment such as jackets, shrouds, hoods, and doors; and ensure they are closed (see Provision of acoustic enclosures)

- use of hoardings or screens as noise barriers erected before any construction activities are undertaken

- plant should be located, as far as is reasonably practicable, away from receptors or as close as possible to noise barriers or hoardings where these are located between the source and receptor (see Provision of acoustic enclosures)

- use of solid doors and gates which should not be located opposite sensitive receptors. The operation of gates should be controlled to minimise the time they are open for the passage of vehicles, thereby minimising stray noise emissions

- that all plant is maintained regularly to comply with relevant national or international standards

- that airlines are maintained and checked regularly to prevent leaks

- plant should be operated in the mode of operation that minimises noise emissions

- that plant is shut down when not in use

- prohibiting works vehicles waiting or queuing on the public highway

- that temporary infrastructure (eg haul roads) should be constructed of materials that minimise noise and vibration (eg laying a tarmac surface)

- that percussive piling shall not be permitted, except where there is an over-riding justification

- use of bending as opposed to percussion methods to break out concrete. Rotary drills and bursters actuated by hydraulic or electrical power should be used for excavating hard material

- handling all materials, particularly steelwork, in a manner which minimises noise. For example storing materials as far as possible away from sensitive receptors and using resilient mats around steel handling areas

- designing all audible warning systems and alarms to minimise noise. Non-audible warning systems shall be utilised in preference, ie cab-mounted CCTV or the use of banksmen. If required, ensure that audible warning systems are switched to the minimum setting required by the HSE, and where practicable use "white noise" reversing alarms in place of the usual "siren" style reversing alert.

- designing haul routes to minimise the amount of reversing required

- electrically powered plant is quieter than diesel or petrol-driven plant, so should be selected if interchangeable

- suitable anti-vibration mountings fitted where practicable, to rotating and/or impacting equipment.

Prior consent

For some construction projects especially projects in residential/built up areas, it is advisable to make an application for consent under Section 61 of **CoPA 1974** to the relevant local authority before works begin. The advantages of applying for a Section 61 are:

- the project can programme works without the risk of local authority intervention

- the risk of delay costs due to abatement action can be reduced

- the formal acceptance by the local authority that BPM has been adopted.

Should you breach the conditions of your Section 61 the following can occur:

1   The local authority can serve a *notice* under Section 60 of **CoPA 1974** or a *nuisance abatement notice* under Section 80 of the **Environmental Protection Act 1990** on the project (not applicable in Scotland).

2   A resident can request a magistrate to serve an *abatement notice* under Section 82 of the **Environmental Protection Act 1990**. However, this is very rare given that the normal procedure is for complaints to go to the local authority (not applicable in Scotland).

It should be noted that the adoption and employment of BPM is a defence against such a notice but, if the construction method and mitigation has not been agreed with the local authority, notice may still be served.

Pre-construction noise monitoring

Before the works start the ambient and background noise levels at locations around the site should be monitored as part of a noise survey. The results should be used to plan the location of noisy operations that could cause nuisance to sensitive receptors, and can be used to oppose any unsubstantiated complaints.

On-site management

On-site management should continue beyond the planning stage taking the good practices and BPM measures identified to minimise noise and vibration, and ensuring that they are adopted on site. It is important to note that Section 61 and Section 60 of **CoPA 1974** relate to the need to define the construction method and steps to minimise noise and vibration.

It is important to bear in mind that the legislation relates to the construction methods themselves. Noise on site should be managed through:

- inspections ensuring that BPM has been adopted (eg correct working hours)
- monitoring to confirm noise level of site activities
- identifying and reporting non-BPM practices, so they can be rectified
- revisioning working practices to ensure that BPM is adopted at all times
- repeating inspections at regular intervals during the project, but more frequently during particularly noisy activities.

Community liaison should be undertaken in advance of works to provide information on what activities you will be doing on site, the reasons why these works are needed and the duration of noisy activities.

Information should be sought from the community concerning sensitive periods (eg school exams), so works can be planned to occur outside these times. If working times have been agreed, ensure that these are adhered to. Through good relations, the potential for complaints or civil claims in the long-term may be reduced. It is especially important to avoid unexpected early starts in the mornings.

It is important to remind site personnel of their obligation to minimise noise and vibration on site. This can be achieved in the site inductions, toolbox talks and through signage onsite (see example in Figure 3.5.1 right).

Figure 3.5.1: On site signage highlighting need to reduce noise –Channel Tunnel Rail Link C105

3.5 Noise and vibration

Construction method audits

During construction, audits should be undertaken to ensure that the noise and vibration minimising methods, plant and mitigation identified in the planning stage are adopted on site.

Formalised auditing should be undertaken by operatives at all times. It may occur at the same frequency and in conjunction with any health and safety review (probably once a week). It is recommended that, if applicable, construction method audits should be integrated into any health and safety or quality surveillance regime.

Noise monitoring

The need to undertake noise monitoring may be a requirement of the contract or may arise out of a consent agreement with the local authority. Although **CoPA** is mainly used in relation to construction site noise, the provisions of the **Environmental Protection Act 1990** must not be ignored either.

It is recommended that noise monitoring be undertaken at the start of each new activity. This may mean that monitoring is required on a daily basis during the first weeks of a construction project and, subject to satisfactory results, could be relaxed to once a week/twice-weekly depending upon the site activities. The frequency should be increased again if particularly noisy activities (such as driven piling) are undertaken.

The monitoring data can be used to assess compliance with any noise limits specified within a Section 60 notice, noise level predictions within a Section 61 consent application, or change in noise levels compared with any pre-construction noise monitoring.

The duration of the monitoring on any one day is important. BS 5228 suggests that the average noise level over a day can be approximated within certain tolerances by taking short-term measurements throughout the day, eg five minutes in every hour.

Noise monitoring should be undertaken only by suitably-trained and experienced personnel. The following information is given to help site personnel ensure monitoring is being properly carried out.

How to measure

Use a Type 1 sound level meter (or Type 2 if specifically allowed for in any specification). The sound level meter types are defined within BS EN 60651:1994(13) according to the precision (or tolerance) to which they measure.

To measure L_{Aeq} values, an integrating-averaging sound-level meter should be used. The relevant standard is BS EN 60804:1994(14), and precision is graded as for normal sound level meters.

The sound level meter should be calibrated before and after measurement. If the calibration is shown to vary by more that +/- 0.5 dB it is advised that the measurements are retaken.

Protect the microphone with a foam windshield. Where measurements are to be taken in poor weather conditions consider using an all-weather microphone protection capsule. Although it is possible to hold the meter in the hand for spot checks, it is preferable to mount the meter on a suitable tripod.

Where to measure

Legislation or consent conditions may specify where measurements should be made, for example at 1m from the nearest sensitive receptor or at the site boundary or 1m from the site boundary. Atmospheric conditions will have an effect on the measured noise level.

Noise measurements should not be taken:

- when wind speed is greater than 5 m/s
- during any rain, hail, etc

The microphone should be positioned approximately 1.2 m – 1.5 m above the local ground height.

The following information should be noted for all noise measurements:

1   Note the construction activities that you are monitoring.
2   A site plan, showing the location of the measurement points denoting whether they are free-field (3.5 m away from a reflecting surface) or façade levels (within 1 m of a building) – methods illustrated overleaf.

Figure 3.5.2: *Façade noise measurement apparatus – Arup*

Figure 3.5.3: *Free-field noise measurement apparatus – Arup*

3 A detailed description of the monitoring position (height, microphone orientation, etc).

4 The date and time at which all measurements are taken.

5 Atmospheric conditions with respect to temperature, wind and rain.

6 Note any other sources of noise not related to the works that are causing high levels of noise.

7 Calibration levels at the beginning and end of the measurement period.

8 The duration of all measurements taken.

9 The noise and vibration indices being measured eg LAeq, LAmax, LA90, etc.

10 The response of the meter eg slow, fast or impulse.

11 Make, model and serial number of all monitoring equipment used.

12 The name and designation of the person taking the readings.

For long-term and possibly unmanned monitoring, take extra care in locating the measurement equipment in order to minimise the risk of damage, theft and the influence of other external noise sources, ie fixed building services plant.

Why is vibration management important?

High vibration levels over a sustained period can cause damage to buildings, while lower vibration levels can cause disturbance to residents. By properly informing local residents of the likelihood that vibration will occur the less likely they are to complain.

As a general guide to acceptable limits for vibration in buildings, the guidance in BS 6472, *Evaluation of human exposure to vibration in buildings*, suggests that levels of vibration below 0.1–0.2 mm/s will normally be imperceptible to people in most situations. This should be the target level. In exceptional circumstances, higher levels may be allowable provided the levels do not exceed those deemed to be limiting values for damage to buildings.

How to avoid vibration problems

The primary aims in the management of vibration on site are to avoid:

- causing annoyance and concerns
- being falsely accused of causing damage
- causing damage to nearby structures

The following six steps will help in addressing each of these aims.

STEP 1 Evaluate the potential for vibration and thereby damage

Transmission of vibration is highly dependent on ground conditions and on features in the ground, such as pipe runs. Prediction methods do exist, but they require specialist expertise to implement and rely on detailed information being available on the site, the ground conditions and the plant.

Guidance regarding vibration damage and human response to vibration are contained within British Standards, BS 7385: Parts 1 and 2, and BS 5228: Part 4.

If it appears that a piling or ground engineering project will generate vibrations putting adjacent structures at risk, then a detailed study should be undertaken by specialists. In most situations it should be sufficient for personnel to review the operations to take place on site and establish the sensitive areas around the site that may need to be monitored.

STEP 2 Monitor conditions before works start

Before starting the construction operations, it is important to survey sensitive locations and structures. The survey should include a detailed record of:

- existing cracks and their widths
- level and plumb survey, including damp-proof course measurements of tilting walls or bulges
- other existing damage including loose or broken tiles, pipes, gullies or plaster.

Photographic records and installation of measurable devices are helpful to establish alleged or actual damage. In some situations it will be necessary to strengthen vulnerable off-site structures before vibrations start.

Sensitive locations to survey and monitor before and during construction would include:

- schools
- hospitals and nursing homes
- historic buildings
- museums
- laboratories
- precision machine workshops

- sensitive plant or equipment used by local companies
- housing
- buildings in poor condition
- brittle/ancient underground services including tunnels

STEP 3 Inform neighbours

Vibration causes anxiety and annoyance to residents mostly because they fear that it will cause damage. It is useful to explain to people that damage only occurs at vibration levels many times greater than those that can be felt from construction plant.

Informing neighbours of the potential for vibration allows site personnel to learn of any particularly sensitive issues that may be time-dependent and that may be resolved by limiting hours of work.

STEP 4 Minimise effects during works

The adoption of BPM means to minimise noise and vibration should have identified the best low vibration method for the completion of a construction task. If there are further concerns about the vibration impact of a construction method then they should be revisited at this stage.

The following specific BPM measures should be considered:

1   Can the activity be undertaken using a different methodology which results in lower levels of vibration at the nearby sensitive receptor?

2   As high frequency vibration causes less damage than low frequency vibration, can the plant be operated in a mode which generates less low frequency vibration, i. vibratory roller, wacker-plates?

3   Can the plant be isolated from the transfer medium (ie what it's sitting on)?

4   Can plant be placed on a heavy base which causes less vibration than plant on a lighter base, eg mount plant on the ground rather than on suspended structures?

Case study

Sheet piles were required to be installed adjacent to an oil testing facility using high precision instrumentation susceptible to vibration. Due to space constraints the work couldn't be undertaken by bored piles and, initially, it was proposed that the piles would be installed by vibratory methods  (impact methods being discounted due to noise issues). However, due to the oil testing facility the sheet piles were installed using hydraulic pile press method which is a very low noise and vibration generating method.

Figure 3.5.4:   *(Above) Hydraulic pile press attached to a leader rig – Arup*

STEP 5 **Monitor vibration levels during the works**

To be effective, monitoring of vibration levels need to be carried out by trained personnel or by external specialists. However, it may be necessary for site personnel to discuss with building occupants where vibration monitoring can be conducted.

The two main rules are that when monitoring at properties during operations:

• measure inside rooms when assessing for nuisance

• measure on the structure outside when assessing for damage (doorsteps are a good location).

Do not forget that in sensitive structures continued visual monitoring and measurement of crack widths is the best way to determine whether damage is being caused.

STEP 6 Monitor conditions after works are completed

The same evaluation as undertaken for Step 2 should be carried out and results compared to the precondition surveys.

Checklist – Noise and vibration: the need to control it	
Noise	
Change the working method to use equipment or modes of operation that produce less noise. For example: ■ in demolition works use hydraulic shears in place of hydraulic impact breakers ■ in driving steel sheet piles consider the jacking method (subject to soil conditions, eg cohesive soils), which produce only a fraction of the noise of conventional hammer-driven piling ■ when breaking out pavements consider other methods than pneumatic breakers and drills, including chemical splitters or falling weight breakers	
Reduce the need for noisy assembly practices, eg fabricate off site	
Keep noisy plant as far away as possible from sensitive receptors	
Adopt working hours to restrict noisy activities to certain periods of the day	
Arrange delivery times to suit the area – daytime for residential areas, perhaps night time for inner-city areas	
Route construction vehicles to take account of the need to reduce noise and vibration	
Keep haul roads well maintained	
Use mufflers or silencers to reduce noise transmitted along pipes and ducts	
Minimise the drop height into hoppers, lorries or other plant (reducing the drop height by a factor of 10 reduces noise by about 10 dB)	
Consider using rubber linings on tippers in very sensitive sites	
Liaise with nature conservation bodies to minimise noise disturbance (disruption) to any sensitive wildlife	

Checklist – Noise and vibration: the need to control it (continued)	
Screens	
Where possible, place sources of noise away from sensitive receptors	
Avoid sound-traps that amplify noise	
Erect the screen close to the source of noise	
Build the screen from materials with density of $7kg/m^2$ or higher, with panels stiffened to prevent drumming	
For the most effective results build the screen about 1 m above the highest sight line	
Seal all gaps and openings, including gaps at the bottom of the screen	
Glaze any public observation openings in perimeter hoardings with Perspex (protected with wire mesh or similar) if sensitive receptors are lower than the height of the hoarding	
Consider placing additional screens close to sensitive receptors but not parallel to nearby walls	

Vibration	
Change the working method to use equipment or modes of operation that produce less vibration, for example ■ breaking out concrete, where practicable, should be undertaken using equipment which breaks concrete by bending rather than by percussion ■ where practicable, rotary drills and bursters actuated by hydraulic or electrical power shall be used for excavating hard material	
Undertake vibration activities as far away as possible from sensitive receptors	
Adopt working hours to restrict high vibration generating activities to certain periods of the day	
Suitable anti-vibration mountings should be fitted where practicable to rotating and/or impacting equipment	
Keep haul roads well maintained	
Consider using rubber linings on tippers in very sensitive sites	

Key guidance

British standards

BS 5118: *Noise control on construction and open sites, Part 4 – Code of practice for noise and vibration control applicable to piling operations*

BS 5228 (1997) *Noise control on construction and open sites*

BS 6472 *Evaluation of human exposure to vibration in buildings*

BS 7385-2:1993 *Evaluation and measurement for vibration in buildings. Guide to damage levels from groundborne vibration*

Other guidance

How much noise do you make? A guide to assessing and managing noise on construction sites, CIRIA PR70

Noise Control: principles and practice – Bruel and Kjoer (Naerum, Denmark), 1982

A guide to reducing the exposure of construction workers to noise, CIRIA R120

The use of screens to reduce noise from sites, CIRIA SP38.

Legislation

A brief summary and interpretation of the legislation relevant to construction activities can be found free of charge on the Internet at www.netregs.org

Additionally CIRIA has produced supporting good practice advice for construction which is available free of charge at www.ciria.org/complianceplus

Environmental Protection Act 1990 (not applicable in Scotland)

Under Section 80 the local authority (Environmental Health Officer) must serve an abatement notice; under Section 82 an individual may obtain an abatement order through a court. A breach of either an abatement notice or an order from the court is a summary offence, punishable by a fine of up to £20 000.

Some local authorities have been known to invoke a Section 80 abatement notice, with potentially more severe consequences than those normally associated with a breach of a Section 60 notice under **CoPA 1974**. *In addition, any person is able to seek an injunction in a civil court: under common law, noise has long been recognised as a nuisance by "interfering with the enjoyment of one's premises".*

Control of Pollution Act (CoPA) 1974

A Section 61 consent should be applied for from the local authority before works begin. This specifies what plant and machinery may be used, the working hours and acceptable noise levels.

A local authority can serve a Section 60 notice if the conditions of the Section 61 consent are breached or if there is no Section 61 in place and excessive noise is being produced.

In Northern Ireland, similar provisions are made to Section 60/61 in the **Pollution Control and Local Government (Northern Ireland) Order 1978**.

3.5 Noise and vibration

Noise at Work Regulations 1989

These regulations, made under the **Health & Safety at Work Act 1974**, detail provisions for the protection of people's hearing while in the workplace. Various levels of acoustic exposure are specified which, when exceeded, determine the level of protection required. Failure to comply with the specifications may lead to prosecution under the **Management of Health and Safety at Work Regulations 1999 (the Management Regulations)**.

Construction Plant and Equipment (Harmonisation of Noise Emission Standards) Regulations 1985 and 1988

An EC examination certificate is required before any item of construction plant and equipment may be marketed. Construction plant and equipment must carry an EC mark to indicate that it conforms to the levels given in the regulations for that type of machinery. Failure to comply with, or contravention of, the regulations may result in a fine of up to £2000.

Other relevant legislation

SI 1968, 1985 *Construction Plant and Equipment (Harmonisation of Noise Emission Standards) Regulations*

SI 361, 1988 *Construction Plant and Equipment (Harmonisation of Noise Emission Standards) Regulations*

SI 1127, 1989 *Construction Plant and Equipment (Harmonisation of Noise Emission Standards) (Amendment) Regulations*

SI 488, 1992 *Construction Plant and Equipment (Harmonisation of Noise Emission Standards (Amendment) Regulations*

SI 3073, 1992 *Machinery (Safety) Regulations (EC Directive 89/392/EEC and subsequent amendments)*

EC directive 70/157/EEC 1970 as amended by 84/424/EEC and 92/97/EEC which specifies maximum drive by noise emissions for road vehicles.

Supplementary information can be found by referring to:

In this handbook	On accompanying CD
Construction process	
4.3, 4.6, 4.7, 4.9, 4.10, 4.14, 4.15, 4.18	Toolbox talks: 3, 4, 13, 18

Why traffic management and vehicle use is important?

It is important to manage traffic and vehicles on site as their mismanagement can cause a nuisance to local residents in terms of noise, dust, congestion and inconvenience through road closures. Traffic management applies to both vehicular and pedestrian traffic and it is the duty of everyone on site to ensure they act responsibly when coming to site, when on site and when leaving site.

Traffic management plan (TMP)

The aim of a TMP is to put in place procedures to manage effectively traffic on site and in the immediate vicinity. The key areas identified in the plan should be reviewed by the site team on a regular basis and with sub-contractors before beginning their works on site and will be updated as necessary. For details on what information should be included in a site TMP refer to the checklist at the end of this Section.

Times during the day when deliveries should not arrive at site should be specified before works start on site. This, for example, would be the morning and afternoon periods of the "school run". However, if deliveries need to be made during these periods alternative routes should be sought and approved by all appropriate parties. This will minimise the local nuisance, congestion of roads and reduce the risk of incidents. The plan should also aim to minimise the number of journeys occurring during working hours by ensuring deliveries are scheduled only when materials are needed.

Traffic and access routes

It is important to manage site traffic, because it can cause delays to local traffic and create a safety hazard both on and off site. People living and working near the site are also often annoyed by the emissions, noise and visual intrusion of queuing vehicles. It is therefore important to develop a clear and simple map to be given to all delivery drivers highlighting the route they must follow to get to the site.

3.6 Traffic management and vehicle use

Access routes

The use of public roads for site access may be restricted. Such restrictions may include:

- weight and width controls
- parking controls
- low-headroom access routes
- accessibility for pedestrians.

Consult with the local police and local authority to address these issues and agree on a workable site access that does not compromise public safety. Plans may be required to identify each access point, the agreed route to the nearest main road, and the routes to be used by lorries to the road network.

Wherever possible, arrange the access so that all vehicles enter and exit the site in a forward direction.

Managing site traffic

Plan the timing of deliveries to avoid vehicles waiting. Where several deliveries are likely to take place over a short period, designate queuing areas away from sensitive receptors. In urban areas it may be best to allocate a waiting area some distance from site and then call in deliveries when access to the site is clear.

Sometimes construction sites are blamed for disturbance caused by vehicles that are not even associated with that site. To avoid this, it may be helpful if site vehicles have visible a badge to identify them as being connected with the project. While this may not be appropriate for individual deliveries it can be done for the main contractors' vehicles and for regular delivery vehicles.

Site worker traffic

Site personnel should not be permitted to park vehicles around the site boundary as this will cause a nuisance to local residents and lead to disruption to deliveries. Arrange designated parking areas when there is appropriate space to do so on larger projects.

On more confined sites this may not be possible, so workers should be encouraged to vehicle share, or arrangements should be made for a minibus to collect them from local train or bus stations. Local employees should be encouraged to walk or cycle (ensure that facilities such as secure areas to store bikes during the working day are made available).

Checklist – Traffic management and vehicle use	
Traffic management plan	
Identify sensitive areas (eg schools and homes)	
Be aware of road restrictions either through road works, narrow roads and bridges with height and/or weight restrictions	
Choose suitable materials for use on access roads – to avoid mud and dust on roads	
Have the details of other developments whose activities could impact on the project	
Identify the locality of suitable parking facilities for private cars and plant	
Ensure there are designated walkways on and around site	
Ensure there are designated vehicular routes on site with speed restrictions	
Locate site entrance and exit so they are not off minor roads	
Gain permission for road closure from the highways division of local authority in smaller scale projects (Highways Agency for larger project)	
Ensure road closures are carried out by a competent person	
Develop a map showing delivery drivers' routes to site from trunk roads	
Schedule site deliveries outside times of peak traffic volume	
Have designated personnel on site to receive deliveries, direct vehicles on and off site, and act as banksman	
Project vehicles should have a badges on their windscreens displaying contact details for the project should they be found to be parked inappropriately	
Offer alternative modes of transport for personnel to site, eg use of minibuses, car sharing or bicycles	
Identify alternative delivery streams, eg canals and railway if feasible	
Monitor vehicle movements to reduce the likelihood of queuing or causing congestion in and around the local area	

Parking	
Designate an area on site for site personnel parking	
Prevent delivery vehicles from queuing outside the site boundary	
Make delivery drivers aware of traffic restrictions on and around the site	

Checklist – Traffic management and vehicle use (continued)	
Plant and vehicles	
Use a wheel wash for vehicles leaving the site to prevent mud being spread on surrounding roads	
Prohibit vehicle washing on site	
Ensure that exhausts do not discharge directly at the ground	
Use retractable sheeted covers to protect wind-blown material	
Ensure all plant and vehicles are in good working order	
Reverse sirens – consider lorries with "white noise" alarms to minimise noise impact on local residents	
Should emergency maintenance need to be carried out on site, ensure it is in a designated area away from sensitive receptors and that a spill kit is close to hand	

Delivery Schedule	
All deliveries to site should keep to their allocated time slot. Failure to do so could mean they are turned away	
No deliveries will be accepted on site without contractor personnel to unload them or direct the vehicle	
No materials or rubbish are to be left in the unloading area	
Washout must occur only in designated areas	
All vehicle delivery drivers are to wear PPE once inside the delivery area	
Incorrectly loaded vehicles will not be offloaded	
During unloading, ropes and fixing devises should be removed with caution. WARNING: risk of load slipping when ropes removed	

Checklist – Traffic management and vehicle use (continued)	
Site rules for drivers	
Access to and from the site will be only via the main entrance gates	
On leaving the site, vehicles to follow the directions previously given	
All engines to be switched off while waiting to unload	
No parking in residential streets surrounding the site	
All drivers are asked to proceed with caution particularly at peak school times in the vicinity of local schools	
Drivers must adhere to the site speed limit	
All vehicles entering the site must stop and report to the gateman who will direct them to the required place of loading/unloading	
Avoid the need to reverse where possible, otherwise a competent banksman must be present	
While on site, drivers are asked to remain in their cabs at all times, unless operating vehicle sheeting mechanism or using the welfare facilities	
Drivers are asked to park in the designated area and wear appropriate PPE (safety helmet, boots and hi-viz jackets) while away from their vehicles	
All loaded vehicles leaving site must be sheeted – this should be done using an "Easy Sheet" mechanism before entering the wheel wash	
All vehicles MUST pass through the wheel wash facility and be inspected by the gateman to ensure they are clean before leaving site	
All loaded vehicles leaving site must take the correct documentation with them. Ensure relevant copies of documentation, together with a copy of the weighbridge ticket, are handed to the gateman on your return to site	

Legislation

A brief summary and interpretation of the legislation relevant to construction activities can be found free of charge on the Internet at www.netregs.org

Additionally CIRIA has produced supporting good practice advice for construction which is available free of charge at www.ciria.org/complianceplus

Highways Act 1980

The **Highways Act 1980** ensures, as far as is reasonably practicable, that the highway is kept in a clear and unobstructed condition for the highway user. Anyone contravening the Highways Act is advised accordingly that any obstruction must be removed. Action may on occasion result in legal proceedings against the person contravening the Act. Contraventions include:

- causing an obstruction on the road   – penalty fine up to **£1000**
- causing vehicular damage to the kerb or footway   – fine **£1000**
- causing an obstruction to pedestrians   – **£1000**
- driving over a footway or a verge   – cost of reinstating footway
- siting a skip dangerously or without permission   – **£1000**
- mixing mortar, cement or concrete on the road or footway   – **£2500**
- posting notices on highway structures or trees   – **£2500**

New Roads and Street Works Act 1991 (NRSWA)

In addition to duties under the **Highways Act 1980**, the local authority, as "street authority", has a duty to coordinate works on the highway, including their works and those of statutory undertakers eg gas.

This role is undertaken in the interests of safety, public convenience, the protection of the structure of the street and the integrity of apparatus in it. The local authority has a duty to ensure all traffic management and re-instatements are carried out effectively and efficiently to keep disruption to the highway user to a minimum.

The council also has some powers regarding the timing of street works and the restriction of such works within 12 months of the completion of substantial road works.

Supplementary information can be found by referring to:

In this handbook	On accompanying CD
Construction process	
4.3, 4.6, 4.7, 4.9, 4.10, 4.15, 4.18	▪ DTI voluntary code of practice for site waste management plans ▪ Environment Agency waste transfer note ▪ Environment Agency hazardous waste consignment note and notification form ▪ European Waste Catalogue Toolbox talks 3, 8, 9, 24

What is waste?

Legally, waste is defined as *"any substance or object which the holder discards, intends to discard, or is required to discard."* This includes materials that other people want, or for which they can find a beneficial use.

Definitions of different types of waste

The European Waste Catalogue (EWC) 2002 can be used to identify your waste and assign a six digit code to it, which helps to determine how to dispose of your waste. Under the Duty of Care six digit codes are now required to be written on waste transfer notes. For the purposes of landfill disposal wastes can be sub-divided into the following:

Inert waste covers materials that do not undergo significant physical, chemical or biological reactions or cause environmental pollution when deposited in a landfill under normal conditions. These include rocks, ceramics, concrete, masonry and brick rubble, but not topsoil.

Non-hazardous wastes are those that are not inert wastes (see above) and include timber and bitumen (depending on tar content). Non-hazardous waste is subject to a higher rate of Landfill Tax than inert waste.

Hazardous wastes are wastes that possess one or more of the 14 hazardous properties in the Hazardous Waste Directive, including those that are deemed to be dangerous to life and/or damaging to the environment, and may be corrosive, reactive, explosive, oxidising, carcinogenic or flammable. Examples of hazardous wastes include asbestos, acids, alkaline solutions, oily sludges, waste oils and wood preservatives.

3.7 Waste

Hazardous wastes can be identified in the **List of Waste Regulations 2005.**

The controls over hazardous wastes were defined within the **Special Waste Regulations 1996.** These regulations have been superseded in England and Wales by the **Hazardous Wastes (England and Wales) Regulations 2005 on 16 July 2005,** but still apply in Scotland. For further details on how hazardous waste has now been sub-divided under these new regulations refer to managing hazardous waste section.

The requirements of the Hazardous Waste Directive have led to legislative amendments in other parts of the UK. For example, in Scotland, the **Special Waste Amendment (Scotland) Regulations 2004** address issues pertinent to hazardous waste and European Waste Catalogue.

Why is the control of waste important?

Managing waste

By identifying potential waste streams that could arise during the various stages of a construction project, there is a greater likelihood that these materials will be reused as a resource. The DTI has developed a Site Waste Management Plan (SWMP) voluntary code of practice. Managing waste on site in accordance with this code will ensure waste is dealt with in accordance with legislation and that best practice is followed.

> A contractor in Cambridgeshire was fined £2250 for illegally depositing waste material consisting of soil and other rubble excavated from a petrol filling station onto land in the area.

Damage to the environment

Annually the UK construction industry generates more than 90 million tonnes of construction and demolition waste – excluding excavation spoil. *(Source: Environment Agency).* Per person, this is about four times the amount of household waste generated. There are environmental and social impacts of dealing with these wastes. For example, noise and traffic emissions that would not arise if the waste was not produced.

Construction and demolition waste accounts for 30 per cent of all fly tipping incidents the Environment Agency deals with. The Environment Agency has reported that 120 000 tonnes of building site waste was fly tipped in just over a year in the Greater London area alone. The Environment Agency and SEPA deal

CIRIA C650

with large scale fly-tipping and hazardous waste, while local authorities deal with smaller scale incidents, abandoned vehicles and litter.

> A Kent haulier was ordered to pay more than £7500 in February 2004 after one of his 20-tonne tipper trucks was caught on CCTV while being used to fly tip construction and demolition waste in Greenwich.

Managing wind-blown solid wastes

Prevent litter and other lightweight materials from blowing off site or into watercourses by storing in enclosed skips and cover over material that has been stockpiled. If work is being undertaken on or near airports, litter and other lightweight material can lead to foreign object damage (FOD) by being sucked into engines.

Impact on project programme and budget

Handling waste inefficiently will cost time, money and effort. For example, by not segregating waste initially, inert material may have to be disposed of as hazardous waste. People often think that waste costs are related only to its disposal. In fact, the true cost of waste is often between 8–10 times the disposal costs and includes:

- purchase price of materials that are being wasted
- cost of storage, transport and disposal of waste
- cost of the time spent managing and handling the waste
- loss of income from not reusing waste materials.

3.7 Waste

The waste hierarchy

Waste management priorities and practical actions that can be undertaken on site should follow the principles of the waste hierarchy as illustrated below:

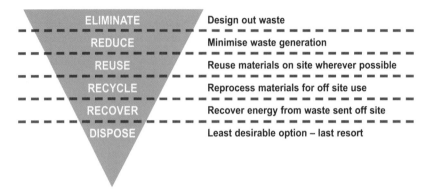

ELIMINATE	Design out waste
REDUCE	Minimise waste generation
REUSE	Reuse materials on site wherever possible
RECYCLE	Reprocess materials for off site use
RECOVER	Recover energy from waste sent off site
DISPOSE	Least desirable option – last resort

Figure 3.7.1: *The waste hierarchy*

Reducing the amount of waste going to landfill

Minimise disposal costs by reusing and recycling wastes generated on site wherever possible. At the design stage of a project use the waste hierarchy to ensure material is reused where appropriate and therefore, does not become waste. If the reuse of material is not considered at the design stage, and during construction the material is placed elsewhere on site, then a waste management licence exemption could be required, accruing extra costs to the project. Exemption is also required if any processing of material (eg sorting, crushing or screening) occurs in accordance with the WRAP quality protocol.

Before stockpiling wastes on site for reuse or recycling, identify where the material is going to be used. If you do not have space on site to segregate wastes for reuse or recycling, consider off site recycling by using a waste management sub-contractor that has the necessary facilities. Consider the use of reused and recycled materials on site. To find sources of such materials talk to local demolition contractors and local authority recycling officers.

Be aware that there may be restrictions on the reuse and recycling of certain materials in some applications (refer to the environmental regulator and the key guidance section for information).

Waste types with potential to be reused or recycled on site:

- concrete
- blacktop
- excavation spoil
- topsoil
- timber

- metals
- architectural features
- clay, concrete pipes, tiles, blocks and bricks
- packaging and plastics.

For more details on wastes that can be reused or recycled refer to the WRAP *Quality protocol for the production of aggregates from inert waste* found on the accompanying CD.

CIRIA has set up a database of recycling facilities across the UK where companies can sell inert materials produced by the construction process and processed aggregates can be purchased. Visit www.ciria.org/recycling/ for further details.

Prefabricated materials constructed off site are generally preferable to those constructed on site, since wastage can be controlled more efficiently and transport requirements are usually reduced.

Waste management on site

Waste management should start with resource efficiency, using the raw goods you purchase wisely. To manage wastes effectively, focus on:

- ordering the correct amount of materials to be delivered when needed
- ensuring materials are not delivered to site damaged and unusable
- reducing the amount of packaging used by suppliers
- establishing a "take back" system with suppliers
- ensuring wastes are handled and stored correctly
- amount of materials that are wasted due to inefficient processes
- amount of wastes that can be reclaimed
- method of waste disposal
- segregation of "difficult" types of waste at source
- reusing waste materials to reduce the amount of waste going to landfill
- fulfiling requirements of your duty of care – one aspect of this is to visit the site at which your waste is disposed
- ensuring your waste is not fly tipped by following your waste carrier to make sure it is being disposed of correctly or auditing the paper trail.

A Hertfordshire building company whose waste ended up strewn across a car park was fined more than £7000 for a failure to exercise a proper duty of care. The builder had used a waste contractor to remove the waste, but the contractor could not be traced. The building company was traced through papers found in the waste by the Environment Agency.

Planning for site waste

To manage site waste effectively and efficiently it is important to allocate sufficient space and resources. In order to plan waste management, it is helpful to know what type and quantities of wastes are generated on site through all project phases. This information may be obtained either by monitoring wastes on site or by drawing on previous experience – bearing in mind that improvements to waste management practices will probably reduce the volume requiring disposal. For further details refer to the DTI *Site Waste Management Plan (SWMP) voluntary code of practice* found on the accompanying CD.

Monitoring wastes on site

The site manager should allocate responsibility to a nominated individual to carry out waste audits at regular intervals to look at:

- quantities of each type of waste generated, reasons why and its cost implications
- how wastes are being handled and stored
- recommendations for improving waste management.

Carrying out audits will provide valuable information to help set targets for improvement and will show how well waste management initiatives are working on site.

In July 2004 a house builder was fined £15 000 for burning waste without having a license to do so. The waste included plasterboard, wooden planks, boards, pallets, paper, cardboard and plastic bags and containers.

Storage and handling of wastes

Efficient storage and handling of waste should include segregation, which has the following benefits:

- easier to see what types of waste are being produced
- enables identification of where efforts to reduce waste need to be targeted
- can reduce landfill tax payments
- maximises the potential for reusing and recycling materials.

Be aware that, for more than 90 cubic metres, a waste management licence will be required to store arisings on site in accordance with the **Waste Management Licensing Regulations 1994.**

When waste is being stored on site it is important that the storage areas have clear signage to ensure different wastes are stored in the correct place. EnCams, ICE and Construction Confederation Environmental Forum have developed standardised waste signage. Further details can be found at: www.wasteawareconstruction.org where a poster creator is available to make customised versions.

Wastes requiring specialist services

Certain wastes require specialists to remove and dispose of them when they are found on site, for example asbestos and sharps (see below). Removal of asbestos and sharps needs to be carried out under a "specific method statement" that has been reviewed and approved by the contractor.

Asbestos

Asbestos is a hazardous material that in the past was extensively used in various applications including:

- insulation of pipes and boilers
- fire protection in panels, wall partitions, ceiling panels and around structural steel work
- roof and wall cladding
- gutters, rainwater pipes and water tanks
- reinforced plastics and sealants
- bound in concrete.

During renovation or demolition the asbestos may be disturbed through drilling, cutting and sanding. Such disturbance would release harmful fibres into the atmosphere that could cause serious health problems. If asbestos is found **stop work** immediately and contact a specialist contractor to remove it.

Sharps

Is the collective name for needles, syringes and other objects which can cause potential harm if the skin is pierced. If found on site **do not** touch and call a specialist contractor to remove.

Transport and disposal of wastes

If information is needed on how to dispose of a particular waste (especially hazardous waste), contact the supplier of the raw material or talk to the environmental regulator.

The person on site with responsibility for waste management must be able to describe both the waste kept on site and the waste transported off site. Disposal of waste from site must be carried out only by a registered waste carrier who should be able to provide you with a colour copy of their waste carriers' licence, the details of which you can check with the environmental regulator.

All non-hazardous waste leaving site MUST be accompanied by a waste transfer note, which needs to include the following information for controlled waste:

- description of the waste
- European Waste Catalogue (EWC) code
- how it is contained
- quantity of waste.

Copies of waste transfer notes need to be kept by the waste producer, the waste carrier, waste broker (if applicable) and the waste disposer. These records need to be kept for a minimum of two years for non-hazardous wastes and five years for hazardous wastes.

The transfer note records the transfer of waste between two parties. It does not record the full journey of the waste and there is no requirement to write the site of final disposal or recovery unless that is where the transfer takes place.

An example of a controlled waste transfer note can be found on the accompanying CD. When disposing of hazardous waste this form should be also be completed and accompany the specific hazardous waste consignment notice.

> In July 2004 The Environment Agency successfully prosecuted a waste carrier for two offences. The company was fined £19 000 for illegally disposing waste and a further £4500 for transferring its waste to an unauthorised person. The company also had to pay a further £2333 in costs.

Landfill Tax

Waste disposed of to landfill is subject to landfill tax. Landfill tax is paid on top of normal landfill fees by businesses and local authorities that want to dispose of waste using a landfill site. It is designed to encourage businesses to produce less waste and to use alternative forms of waste management.

The tax applies to materials like waste soil and waste clay that are often sold to the landfill operator for use as daily cover. There are two bands of landfill tax – non-hazardous and hazardous, with hazardous waste subject to a higher tax rate than inert waste. If these are mixed together the higher rate of tax will be charged on the whole load, so segregating waste saves money.

Waste arising from the following activities is exempt, subject to meeting certain conditions:

- some dredging activities
- quarrying and mining
- reclamation of contaminated land.

Managing hazardous wastes

Identify and separate out hazardous wastes that are generated on site. Ensure that everyone who might be exposed to hazardous wastes is aware of their potential effects and what to do with them.

Transport and disposal

Under the **Hazardous Waste (England and Wales) Regulations 2005,** the Environment Agency must be notified of premises (a copy of the form can be found on accompanying CD) where more than 200 kg of hazardous waste will be produced. You can register your site with the Environment Agency either through the Internet (£18), telephone (£23) or paper (£28) per premises. Once a site is registered it will be assigned a unique five digit code which needs to be put on all consignment notes.

The waste producer must complete a hazardous waste consignment note (copy available on accompanying CD) that travels with the waste to its final treatment or disposal option. Information that must be recorded on the consignment note includes:

- premises code
- description of waste
- EWC code
- quantity (kg)
- chemical/biological components of waste and their concentrations
- physical form
- hazardous code(s)
- container type, number and size.

Every consignment removed from site will attract a fee that must be paid by the consignee to the Environment Agency with their quarterly returns. The fees are as follows:

- for multiple collection round consignments – £5 for electronic returns, £10 for postal returns
- for single consignments – £10 for electronic returns, £19 for postal returns.

Before any hazardous waste is removed from site an appropriate treatment or disposal route must be identified. Copies of documentation for the transport of hazardous and other wastes must be retained for five and two years respectively.

Exempt premises

Premises can be exempt from the need to register if they fall into one of the following categories and produce less than 200 kg of hazardous waste annually:

- offices and shops except where they are part of a non-exempt site

- premises where Waste Electrical and Electronic Equipment (WEEE) is collected where the premises are used for that purpose
- schools, prisons, charities
- premises used by a dental, veterinary or medical practice.

In these cases, collections still have to be made by a registered waste carrier using a specific exemption code on the consignment note.

In 2004 the **EU Landfill Directive** resulted in a significant decrease in the number of hazardous waste landfill sites in the UK. This resulted in higher transportation costs and higher gate charges being levied. Check the environmental regulators website to identify the nearest landfill sites that can accept hazardous waste.

The European Waste Catalogue (EWC)

The EWC was produced in 2002 and details a list of wastes and a series of steps for identifying wastes providing a unique six digit code for each. The relevant EWC code(s) must be included on waste transfer notes and consignment notes. The main chapter of the EWC relation to the construction is Chapter 17: *Construction and demolition wastes* (including excavated soil from contaminated sites). A copy of the complete EWC can be found on the accompanying CD.

Waste Acceptance Criteria (WAC)

Wastes can be accepted only at a particular hazardous landfill if they meet the relevant WAC for that class of landfill. There are three stages to assess this:

1   European Hazard Criteria Assessment.
2   Solids Testing.
3   Leaching Testing.

Hazardous Waste (England and Wales) Regulations 2005

These regulations replaced the **Special Waste Regulations 1996 (as amended)** on 16 July 2005 and introduced new and more simple procedures for tracking the movement of wastes. It removes the current need to pre-notify the Environment Agency before hazardous waste can be moved off site, and includes a simpler method of tracking wastes once they have been moved. In Scotland pre-notification is still required to SEPA as the **Special Waste Regulations** still apply.

3.7 Waste

A key requirement of the new regulations is to notify the Environment Agency of any **premises** producing hazardous waste. The regulations improve the management of hazardous waste from cradle to grave. Waste is defined under the regulations as either:

- non-hazardous

- hazardous (mirror entry) – waste that could be hazardous or non-hazardous, depending on its actual composition and concentration of "dangerous substances"

- hazardous (absolute) – waste that is hazardous, regardless of its composition or concentration of "dangerous substances".

The classification of waste and determination of disposal route under the regulations involves the following steps:

1 Use EWC to apply code and classify waste as either non-hazardous, hazardous (mirror entry) or hazardous (absolute).

2 Determine hazard level.

3 Determine WAC test and carry out either on site or at a treatment plant.

4 Demonstrate WAC test results meet legislative requirements.

5 Determine waste disposal route:

- inert waste landfill

- non-hazardous landfill

- non-reactive cell in non-hazardous landfill – asbestos and plasterboard

- hazardous waste landfill.

For further information on managing hazardous waste on site refer to www.hazardouswaste.org.uk

Checklist – Waste	
Storing wastes properly on site	
Segregate waste. Make this easy for site personnel to do, by providing a number of waste containers in a designated waste storage area and briefing them on their requirements	
Mark waste containers clearly with their intended contents. Consider using colour coding/labelling	
Use containers suitable for their contents. Check that containers are not corroded or worn out	
Use covered skips to prevent spread of wind-blown wastes	

Storage of hazardous waste	
Check that your premises are registered as a producer of hazardous waste, if more than 200 kg (applicable in England & Wales not Scotland)	
Ensure hazardous wastes are stored in suitable labelled containers away from sensitive receptors and the risk of damage by site traffic	
Hazardous waste must not be mixed with non-hazardous waste	
Avoid mixing different types of hazardous waste together	
Do not store wastes longer than is necessary to complete documentation to arrange its disposal	

Handling and removing waste (on a confined site)	
If removing waste from upper levels on buildings, transport using roller bins	
Store these bins in an area close to lifts	
Arrange for daily collection of bins	
Lower bins to ground floor only shortly before collection lorry arrives	

Checklist – Waste (continued)	
Duty of care	
Check that you have a copy of the waste carrier's licence on site and that it is still valid. The waste carrier's licence should be accepted only if it has been endorsed by the appropriate environmental regulator	
The waste carrier must be licensed to carry waste	
The transfer notes should be completed in full and contain an accurate description of the waste, full European Waste Catalogue (EWC) code, and signed by the producer and carrier prior to waste leaving the site	
Keep copies of all transfer notes for waste sent off site for two years for inert and five years for hazardous	
Hazardous waste movements must be documented using consignment notes rather than the normal waste transfer note	
Carry out spot checks to ensure compliance with your duty of care including: ▪ following your waste carrier to ensure the waste does arrive at the agreed disposal site ▪ carry out periodic audits on your waste carrier ▪ visit your waste carriers premises ▪ visit agreed disposal site to confirm it is licensed to accept your waste	

Key guidance

Quality protocol for the production of aggregates from inert waste, WRAP

Site waste management plan industry code of practice, DTI

Demonstrating waste minimisation benefits in construction, CIRIA C536

Waste management – the duty of care, code of practice, HMSO

The reclaimed and recycled materials handbook, CIRIA C513

Use of recycling for road pavement construction and maintenance, County Surveyors' Society, 1994

Legislation

A brief summary and interpretation of the legislation relevant to construction activities can be found free of charge on the Internet at www.netregs.org

Additionally CIRIA has produced supporting good practice advice which is available free of charge at www.ciria.org/complianceplus

Waste Management Licensing Regulations 1994

A licence (or exemption) is required if depositing, keeping, treating or disposing of controlled waste in or on land (including the treatment or disposal in mobile plant).

Activities exempt from the need for a licence are defined in Schedule 3 of the regulations and include activities such as reclamation and recycling. If properly operated and managed such activities are considered to pose a lower risk to the environment or health.

Environmental Protection (Duty of Care) Regulations 1991

Under these regulations the waste producer has a responsibility to ensure that waste is disposed of in the correct manner. This includes:

- using licensed waste carrier to dispose of your waste
- filling out and retaining waste transfer notes – retain for two years for inert and non-hazardous waste and five years for hazardous
- ensuring your waste is disposed of at an appropriately licensed disposal facility.

Controlled Waste (Registration of Carriers and Seizure of Vehicles) Regulations 1991 / Controlled Waste (Amendment) Regulations 1993

You have a duty to ensure that your waste is carried by a licensed waste carrier. If you transport waste from site yourself, you must ensure that you have a waste carrier's licence unless you are the producer of the waste being transported.

Landfill (England and Wales) Regulations 2002

These regulations introduced the European Waste Catalogue (EWC) codes and it is the responsibility of the waste producer to use the EWC to allocate a six digit code that most accurately describes their waste when completing waste transfer notes.

The regulations also affect disposal routes for hazardous waste as there are a limited number of landfill sites that are licensed to accept hazardous waste.

The regulations have banned hazardous liquid waste from landfill and all other liquid wastes will be banned by 2007. Since 2003 whole used tyres have been banned from disposal to landfill, with shredded used tyres being banned by July 2006.

Producer Responsibility Obligations (Packaging Waste) Regulations, 1997

The packaging regulations set out requirements for recovery and recycling of waste packaging for organisations with a turnover of >£2 million and which place >50 tonnes of packaging material into the packaging supply chain. In the construction sector this is applicable primarily to materials suppliers.

Special Waste Regulations, 1996 – applies in Scotland and Northern Ireland under Special Waste Regulations (Northern Ireland) 1998

Under these regulations the waste producer has a responsibility to pre-notify SEPA/EHSNI three days before special waste is removed from site.

Hazardous Waste (England and Wales) Regulations 2005

These regulations supersede the Special Waste Regulations and require the waste producer to register with the Environment Agency any premises that produce more than 200 kg of hazardous waste per annum.

Special Waste Amendment (Scotland) Regulations 2004

Applies in Scotland and amends the **Special Waste (Scotland) Regulations 1996**. These amendment regulations transpose the requirements of the Hazardous Waste Directive and take account of the changes in the European Waste Catalogue. The regulations are not exhaustive and can be subject to further amendments or updates.

Supplementary information can be found by referring to:

In this handbook	On accompanying CD
Construction process	
4.2, 4.4, 4.5, 4.8, 4.10, 4.14, 4.21, 4.23, 4.24	▪ Water guide to good practice on site Toolbox talks: 1, 2, 5, 6, 13, 16, 17, 18

Why water management is important?

Controlled waters have legal protection and include rivers, streams, ditches, ponds, locks, groundwater and coastal waters up to three miles offshore. Pollution is any poisonous, noxious or polluting matter or any solid waste matter (which includes silt, cement, concrete, oil, petroleum spirit, chemicals, solvents, sewage or other polluting matter).

It is vital to manage water properly on site to protect the environment and water supplies. If controlled waters are polluted, or unacceptable wastes are disposed of to the sewer system, you, your company, your sub-contractors and your client could end up in court. Additionally, you may be liable for damages to industries utilising water downstream.

The polluter is responsible for paying any fine through strict liability, court costs, and also for the cost of clean-up, which is often greater than the fine. Directors can be held personally responsible and can be fined and imprisoned for up to six months or an unlimited period of indictment.

The site does not need to be next to a river to cause a problem. Any pollutants getting into a surface water drain or groundwater can end up in a river even if it is miles away. These pollutants can be tracked back to their source.

	Five litres of oil can disperse to cover an area of water the size of four football pitches

Environment Agency records show that in the last 10 years, the construction industry in England and Wales has caused more pollution incidents than any other industrial sector, causing an average of 570 pollution incidents per year.

Even a small amount of material can be a pollutant. For example, the normal limits set by the environmental regulator for suspended solids are typically 30–40 mg/l. This is about the equivalent of mixing half a tablespoon of soil in a bath full of water.

During the upgrading of the M74(M) in southwest Scotland, discharges from the construction site into top class, quality salmonid rivers contained suspended solids concentrations as high as 46 800 mg/l. These high concentrations of suspended solids, derived from silt, resulted in the contractors being fined £40 000 for the offences.

High levels of silt can clog the gills of fish and ultimately lead to their death. It can also smother invertebrates and sensitive plant life, which are themselves a food source for fish. When deposited on the stream bed, silt may prevent fish spawning successfully and suffocate eggs. Levels as low as 15 mg/l can harm juvenile fish. Measures to prevent silt from entering water include the provision of splash plates as illustrated by Figure 3.8.1.

Figure 3.8.1: *Temporary bridge & splash plates protect salmonoid stream – SEPA*

A contractor was found liable for causing oil pollution of the Grand Union Canal, after a tap was removed from an oil storage tank. In its defence, the company blamed vandals. Magistrates agreed with the Environment Agency that the site had poor security and the company was fined £7000 and had to pay costs of more than £11 000.

Other pollutants damage the water environment in other ways, for example:

Common pollutants of water	Adverse affect on aquatic environment
Silt	Reduces water quality, clogs fish gills, cover aquatic plants
Bentonite (very fine silt)	Reduces water quality, clogs fish gills, cover aquatic plants
Cement or concrete wash water (highly alkaline)	Changes the chemical balance
Detergents	Removes dissolved oxygen
Hydrocarbons, eg oil, diesel	Suffocates aquatic life

Contaminants that disperse quickly are very difficult to control and treat. They are easily transported in watercourses and the effects are likely to be significant. Some contaminants can smother the surface of watercourses depleting oxygen and leading to fish death. Notify and seek advice from the environmental regulator if spillages occur.

Riparian landowners

If your site is adjacent to a watercourse you are a riparian owner and you have certain rights and responsibilities in relation to the watercourse flowing through or adjacent to your site. The riparian rights include the following:

* ownership of the land up to the centre of the watercourse
* right to protect property from flooding and land erosion
* to receive water of good quality and quantity.

The responsibilities of riparian owners include:

* to pass on the flow of water without obstruction, pollution or diversion affecting the rights of others
* accepting the flood flows though the land
* maintaining the bed and banks of the watercourses including the removal of debris even if it originated elsewhere
* keeping the bed and banks clear of material that could cause obstructions either on the riparian owner's land or by being washed downstream
* keeping culverts, trash screens, weirs and mill gates clear of obstructions.

3.8 Water

Before starting any work on or adjacent to a watercourse, you must submit plans of your proposals to the Environment Agency and the local authority to determine whether you require a consent and/or planning permission. If the work affects sites of known conservation or archaeological value, you may need further permissions from the relevant heritage body. Environmental issues, including flood risk, wildlife conservation, fisheries, and reshaping of the river and landscape, must all be considered.

General good practice

Know your site

Before starting works, carry out surveys to establish the existing water quality and water levels around the site. Establish the location of local streams and mark the position of surface water drains and foul sewers on site. Use colour coding to distinguish them, blue for surface water, red for foul water and a red "C" for combined drainage systems. Carry out regular inspections of all discharge points and associated pipework, drainage systems, collection ditches, lagoons, oil separator (and drip-trays) and watercourses to check that these are in good order.

Look out for underground pipes and tanks and avoid disturbing any underground services or structures.

Abstracting water

If construction activities, for example concrete batching or dust suppression, require water to be abstracted from surface water or groundwater, a licence will be required. Contact the environmental regulator for information.

Discharging water

Discharges should only be made to drains with the appropriate discharge consents:

- foul water sewer – effluent discharge consent required from sewerage provider
- controlled waters (from surface water drains) – discharge consent from environmental regulator.

If the discharge of water is necessary this should be to the foul sewer rather than surface water drain.

Discharge consents can be obtained from the environmental regulator, but can take up to four months to obtain, or even longer if there are representations made by third parties/the public. It is, therefore, important to plan ahead to avoid delays. Even with a consent, allowable pollution limits will be low.

March

Damage to drains and sewers by the use of heavy plant or through digging can cause blockages that may lead to pollution incidents. Protect services before tracking plant over them. There have even been pollution incidents resulting from sewers that are blocked with timber and safety hats!

Water generated on site may be contaminated with pollutants that cannot be discharged to the sewer. Therefore, it will have to be pumped into a tanker and taken off site for disposal adding extra costs to the project. See the flow diagram (Figure 3.8.2) on the next page outlining steps to follow when disposing of water on site.

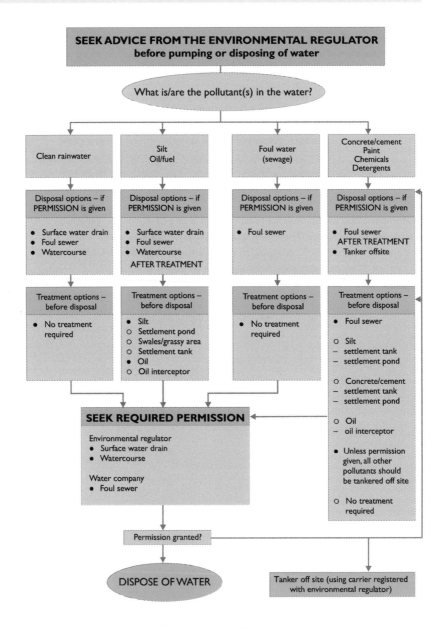

Figure 3.8.2:   *Treatment of site water procedure*

How and what to monitor

The chemical analysis of water samples for trace quantities of contaminants or for particular pollutants is a specialised task. However, much may be learned from the visual appearance of a water sample. The following can give an insight into the potential problems associated with a water sample:

- turbidity – colour
- odour
- presence of oil film.

The use of pH papers and test strips can indicate the presence of specific components on site. For instance, high pH rinse waters from cement batching plants or grouting works can be toxic to aquatic life and may cause a severe pollution incident. This can be identified easily through the use of pH papers which show a colour change in response to differing acidity or alkalinity. These problems can be overcome by chlorination of water to sterilise it.

March

In certain circumstances it makes sense, if spills are possible, to place primary and secondary booms permanently across very sensitive watercourses. Discuss with the environmental regulator where this may apply.

Environmental regulators are generally not keen on flocculants being used as the flocculants themselves can be highly polluting and toxic to river life.

Avoiding spillages
There are many precautions that can be taken to avoid spillages. These are outlined in Section 4, and include:

- use of secondary containment, eg bunds around oil storage tanks – this may be a legal requirement (see Section 4.20)
- use of drip trays around mobile plant (see Section 4.21)
- supervising all deliveries and refuelling
- using specific refuelling areas isolated from surface water drains (see Section 4.22).

Forward planning can ensure a speedy emergency response if things do go wrong. For example, sandbags can be used as a barrier to protect sensitive areas, or block off drains during refuelling. They are also effective for controlling and mopping up spillages. Any absorbent material that becomes contaminated may have to be disposed of as hazardous waste (see Section 3.7).

Emergency preparedness and response

All site personnel should be aware of the appropriate action in the event of an emergency, such as the spillage of potentially polluting substances, and a spill response plan should be developed for the site (see Section 2.4). For details on appropriate fuel storage measures refer to Section 3.2.

Managing effluent from vehicles and boot washing

Wash vehicles and plant at specialist facilities rather than on site. Where this is not possible the following options are shown in order of best environmental option:

- carry out cleaning in a bunded area and recycle the water
- discharge waste water to the foul sewer (with the consent of the sewerage provider)
- collect water in a sealed tank for removal from site by a licensed waste disposal contractor.

Vehicle wheels may need to be washed on site to avoid mud on public roads. A specific wheel washing facility (Figure 3.8.4) should be used which should store the water, with either a discharge to the foul sewer or, if contaminated, collection by tanker.

Figure 3.8.4: *On-site wheel wash facilities – Bovis*

Figure 3.8.5: *On-site bootwash facilities – Morrison*

Facilities should also be provided for site workers to wash their boots (Figure 3.8.5) to remove mud. This is very important on contaminated sites. Again this should follow the procedures in place for vehicle wheel washing.

Do not allow water containing detergents to enter surface water drains or watercourses.

In exceptional circumstances, discharge to surface water may be permitted with the consent of the environmental regulator. However, this would require pre-treatment (for example, silt settlement and oil separation) and it may be difficult to control quality.

March

> If tools and equipment need to be washed, ensure that this is undertaken well away from any watercourse or surface water drains on an area of hardstanding to avoid infiltration of potential pollutants into soils.

Working over or near to water

Consent is required from the environmental regulator for any works over or near to water. Due to the increased risk of water pollution, particular care should be taken. Good practice includes:

- ensuring comprehensive risk assessments have been undertaken, and subsequent risk management plans are implemented
- use of decking/barges below the works (acting as a bund in case of spillage)
- use of primary and secondary booms to contain pollutants in the event of substances entering the water
- erecting dust screens on bridges.

Managing runoff and silty water

Surface water runoff may cause water management or pollution problems. For example, more than 25 tonnes of sediment can be eroded per hectare of site in a year. The solution is to control surface water so that it does not run into excavations, disturbed ground or haul roads (see Section 4.9 and 4.10). Ensure that the water collection system is adequate to allow for the controlled release of storm flows. Protect watercourses from becoming silted as a result of runoff from disturbed ground and soil stockpiles.

Periods of heavy rain can increase dramatically surface water runoff giving very high pollutant loads. Ensure you keep hardstanding areas and surface roads clean from mud and oil build up, and stockpiles covered.

A silt fence can be used to prevent silt from entering watercourses. It comprises a vertical fence about 300–450 mm high made of two layers of woven geotextile welded together. Posts placed between the two layers support the fence. The fence should be dug in slightly, both to prevent runoff escaping underneath it and to give it extra strength. Silt fences can be placed at the toe of stockpiles (about 5 m away from the base) or at the top of banks of watercourses. Collected silt should be cleaned away regularly. Site fences work best if slopes draining to them are less than about 30 m long. The ends should return up the slope to stop flows around the ends.

Do not rely on silt fences to remove sediment from concentrated flows such as pipe discharges and in watercourses.

Considering the options

To establish the best approach for your site, review the following prioritised options; those at the top of the list are least expensive and cause least risk of accidental pollution.

1   Pump to grassland or other soakaway – well away from excavations to avoid recirculation through the ground. The silty water should contain no chemical pollutants.

Cheapest

2   Pump to sewer – consent from the sewage provider is required (see guidance earlier in this Section).

3   Pump to settlement tank maximising retention time.

4   Pass through a filtration system.

5   Use flocculants in conjunction with settlement tank.

6   Pump into a tanker and dispose of off site.

Most expensive

The preferred option will depend on a number of factors, including:

- the quantities of water involved

- whether areas are available for storage and treatment

- the level of any charges to be levied by the sewerage provider

- the degree of contamination of the water

- the characteristics of the sediment.

Silt arising from clay soils is vastly more difficult to remove than sandy particles before discharge to controlled waters. Also, consider the amount of rainfall that is likely in a particular area.

Pumping to grasslands/fields

Obtain the prior approval of the environmental regulator and the landowner before doing anything. This option is really suitable only for water that is unpolluted aside from its silt content. It may also be necessary to allow water temperatures to rise by storing in a lagoon before discharge onto crops. Typical infiltration rates are given below for various soils.

Typical infiltration rates for various soils						
Soil texture	Sand	Sandy loam	Loam	Clay loam	Silty clay	Clay
Infiltration rate (mm/h)	50	25	13	8	3	5
Typical mm/h (range)	(25-250)	(13-75)	(8-20)	(3-15)	(0.3-5)	(1-10)
Typical L/min/ha*	8000	4000	2000	1300	500	800

* Litres per minute per hectare, assuming the water to be spread evenly over the surface. A typical agricultural sprayer discharges at about 1000 l/min.

Settlement tanks/lagoons

A settlement lagoon (or tank) works by retaining water in an undisturbed state long enough for suspended solids to settle out. The clean water then either flows out at the discharge point or is pumped out. It is usually necessary to retain the water in the settlement tank (as shown in Figure 3.8.6) for 2–3 hours at maximum flow rate. However, finer particulate matter (eg fine sand) may require a longer retention time and possibly larger lagoons. An idea of the required retention time can be obtained by leaving a sample of the

Figure 3.8.6: *Settlement lagoon –SEPA*

contaminated water to stand in a clear glass bottle. Compare this sample to a prepared sample of a concentration equal to your consented discharge. As a general rule, when the contaminated water sample looks as clear as the sample representing the consented discharge, it may be discharged.

Typical dimension of a settlement tank/lagoon for a three-hour settling time

Pump diameter	Discharge rate	Length	Width
6 in pump	3000 l/min	60 m	20 m
	6000 l/min	80 m	27 m
4 in pump	1000 l/min	30 m	10 m
2500 l/min	2500 l/min	50 m	17 m

(Assuming 1 m-deep ponds, where the length = three times the width)

Consider installing a spare settlement tank/lagoon on site, so that it can be used as an emergency overflow or when the main tank is being cleaned.

Surface water drainage from a site overflowed from three settlement tanks into a settlement lagoon and then to a consented discharge point in the River Thames (Dagenham Breach). There was a discharge of "very chalky water" from the settlement tanks. The contractor pleaded guilty to "causing polluting matter to enter controlled water". A fine of £1000 was imposed, although it could have been up to £20 000.

Filtration

Discharges with fairly coarse particles and relatively small flows may be treated easily and cheaply by passing them through steel tanks or even skips (as illustrated by Figure 3.8.7) filled with a suitable filter, such as fine single size aggregates (5-10 mm), geotextiles or straw bales. Filtration socks can also be added for additional treatment. If this solution is used there must be careful control of the discharge quality and a mechanism to close down the flow.

Figure 3.8.7: *Water filtration system – Bovis*

Flocculation

If no alternative treatment is available, due to the material characteristics, lack of space or lack of suitable discharge locations, the use of settlement tanks together with flocculant (or coagulant) can be an effective solution, particularly to aid the settlement of fine silts. This approach needs specialist advice on the design of the system, the size and dosing rates etc, and careful supervision to avoid failures of the system. Flocculants commonly used include aluminium sulphate and ferric sulphate, which if applied incorrectly can themselves cause pollution.

Temporary works

In England and Wales, the Environment Agency needs at least seven days notice of any intention to temporarily or permanently divert the flow of a watercourse, carry out works over or within the river channel or begin operations in the river channel.

Obtain prior approval from the Environment Agency for all temporary works that involve construction, erection, re-erection or modification during work which:

- may interfere with the bed or banks or flood channel of any watercourse
- is within 8 m of the bank of any main river
- is within 16 m of any tidal defence.

Similar arrangements are in place in Scotland where SEPA should be given advanced notice.

Checklist – Water

Know your site

Establish water quality by undertaking baseline assessments before work begins on site	
Identify site drainage as surface, combined or foul water and suitably colour code and mark on the site plan	
Protect/cover all drains	
Ensure that the correct connections are being made with either foul sewers, surface water drains or combined systems	
Identify all water bodies, gain appropriate consents and put measures in place to fulfil the requirements of your consent	

Abstracting water

Ensure the site has a licence to abstract water from a controlled water source	
Ensure the site complies with the abstraction licence	

Discharging water

Check that appropriate consents for disposal of all water is in place, and that personnel are aware of the quantity and quality of water that can be discharged	
Check for any visible sign or smell of pollution in watercourses at or near the site	
Water needs to be treated effectively before disposal	
If a settlement tank is being used, check it is working	

How and what to monitor

Establish a regular monitoring procedure for water discharged from the site and keep records (turbidity/flow rate)	
Check outfalls and pipework daily to ensure they are clean and clear of litter, etc	

Avoiding spillages

Store liquids, solids and powders appropriately, and away from drains and watercourses in secondary containment	
Store solvents, chemicals or paints in accordance with their COSHH datasheets	
Appropriate spill kits should be available (eg oil only, chemical or general use) and adequately stocked	

Checklist – Water (continued)

Emergency preparedness and response

Ask site personnel if they know whom to contact in the event of a spillage, what to do and from where to get equipment	
Adopt and test an emergency response plan	
Nominate a spill contractor to deal with major incidents	

Managing effluent

Wash out concrete lorries in a suitably contained designated area	
The designated washout area has to be at least 10 metres away from drains and watercourses	
Protect watercourses and groundwater from washout	
Put a plan in place to dispose of washout cost-effectively	

Managing run-off and silty water

When undertaking earthworks ensure a filter strip been left to protect surface water	
Regularly check watercourses (if applicable)	
Look for any visible signs of discolouration in watercourses (if applicable) at or near the site	
Silty or discoloured water should not be discharged from the site	
Surface water runoff should not be directly entering a watercourse or drain	
Monitor any water treatment methods to ensure their effectiveness	
If a settlement tank is used, see if water is moving too fast and/or overflowing (other than at the discharge point)	
If straw bales are used, ensure they are securely fixed	

3.8 Water

Working over or near to water

Avoid storing fuel in vessels near water	
Check to see if any site works are occurring within 10 m of the edge of watercourses	
Check that the banks or bed of the watercourse outside the area of works is not being affected by discharges or vehicle movements, etc	
Spray, dust or other airborne materials should not enter a watercourse	
Approachways to the watercourse should be kept free from the build up of mud	
If using a cofferdam to retain water, it needs to be in good condition and working effectively	
Check the watercourse to see if it is silty or discoloured downstream of the works or if there is an oily sheen visible on the water	
Ensure spill kits are adequately stocked	
Personnel are to be aware of the location of spill kits and know how to use these properly	
Mitigation measures to be put in place in the event of an emergency (eg booms across river)	

Settlement tank/lagoon

Design	
The size of the tank/lagoon should be adequate for the settlement time required and the rate at which water flows or is pumped into it	
Install a long, narrow, shallow settlement lagoon to ensure maximum retention time of all water in the lagoon	
Operation	
Obtain a consent to pump clean water from the surface of settlement lagoons into rivers or designated discharge point	
Is the entry chamber cleaned periodically to prevent a build-up of silt?	
Periodically monitor the outflow quality	

Checklist – Water (continued)	
Dealing with water in excavations	
Measures should be put in place to prevent water from entering excavations	
Inform the environmental regulator before any excavation below the water table, including any site dewatering	
Control water in excavations by stone-filled edge drains leading to sumps	
To manage groundwater flowing into excavations, install cut off ditches, walls or well point dewatering	
Obtain a discharge consent for water from excavations	
Pontoons and barges	
All fuel tanks to be secure and safe on the vessel so that there is no chance of collision damage or accidental spillage overboard	
Contaminated bilge water should be pumped to suitable facilities ashore or absorbents used	

Key guidance

Regulatory guidance

Pollution prevention guidance notes – 1 to 8, 18, 21, 23, 26, 27 (see Appendix 1).

Environment Agency/CIRIA joint guidance:

Masonry bunds for oil storage tanks

Concrete bunds for oil storage tanks.

Other guidance

Control of water pollution from construction sites. Guidance for consultants and contractors, CIRIA C532

Control of water pollution from construction sites – guide to good practice CIRIA SP156

British Waterways environmental code of practice, British Waterways, 1996

Control of water pollution from linear construction projects, CIRIA Research Project 708 due to be published in 2006.

3.8 Water

Legislation

A brief summary and interpretation of the legislation relevant to construction activities can be found free of charge on the Internet at www.netregs.org

Additionally CIRIA has produced supporting good practice advice which is available free of charge at www.ciria.org/complianceplus

Control of Pollution Act 1974

It is an offence to cause or knowingly permit any poisonous, noxious or polluting matter or any solid waste matter (which includes silt, cement, concrete, oil, petroleum spirit, chemicals, solvents, sewage or other polluting matter) to enter any controlled waters unless a discharge is authorised.

Trade Effluents (Prescribed Processes and Substances) Regulations, 1989 (as amended)

Originally made under the **Water Act 1989**, these regulations prescribe the substances and processes which are treated as "special category effluent" under **Water Industry Act 1991** and require referral to the environmental regulator.

Water Resources Act 1991 in England and Wales or Control of Pollution Act 1974 in Scotland

Consent is required from the environmental regulator before discharging water to any **controlled water** or surface water drain.

Permissions may be required from the environmental regulator or the local authority depending on the precise nature of activities. For example, consents are required for:

1 Removal of vegetation adjoining rivers.

2 Works affecting watercourses.

Water Industry Act 1991 in England and Wales or the Sewerage (Scotland) Act 1968 in Scotland

Consent is required from the local sewerage provider before discharging water to any **foul water sewer**.

Water Environment and Water Services (Scotland) Act 2003 (WEWS)

Introduces the way that the water environment is regulated and managed in Scotland in order to meet the requirements of the European Union Water Framework Directive. WEWS will provide regulation of engineering works, impoundments and abstractions. In addition, WEWS will supersede the process of consenting discharges currently undertaken under the auspices of the **Control of Pollution Act 1974.**

Abstracting water

In England and Wales an abstraction licence is required from the **Environment Agency** if more than 20 cubic metres of water per day will be abstracted from ground or surface waters. For abstraction of water in Northern Ireland contact **EHSNI.**

3.9 Wildlife and natural features

Supplementary information can be found by referring to:

In this handbook	On accompanying CD
Construction process	
4.7, 4.8, 4.9, 4.10, 4.12, 4.13, 4.17, 4.18, 4.19, 4.22	▪ List of protected bird and animal species Toolbox talks: 1, 2, 4, 5, 6, 7, 10, 11, 12, 14, 15, 17, 18, 19, 20, 22

What are wildlife and natural features?

These include trees, plants, insects, birds, fish and mammals as well as their habitats. Rocks and landforms that shape the landscape are also important. Climate, geology or soil structure and land management all influence the creation of habitats and the presence of species in particular locations. It is important to look at individual species, but also at larger animal populations, plant communities, their habitats, the rocks and landforms and the natural processes that affect them.

Why is it important to consider wildlife?

The level of protection given to wildlife is increasing through legal controls and contract conditions. The identification and management of wildlife within a site needs to be undertaken at the planning stage of a project to ensure delays to the programme and extra costs are not incurred.

A responsible attitude should be adopted to ensure construction activities cause the least damage to the surrounding natural environment. Where possible, enhance the natural environment through appropriate habitat creation thereby enhancing biodiversity.

Wildlife surveys

A project can be delayed while waiting for the correct time of year to undertake a wildlife survey of the site. Figure 3.9.1 provides an indication of the best time to undertake wildlife surveys before work begins. This should help to minimise the risk of delays. Surveys may be carried only out at particular times of the year by a professional consultant.

CIRIA C650

Wildlife year planner

Legend:
- Work restricted
- Recommended survey time
- Recommended time to work

Protected species	January	February	March	April	May	June	July	August	September	October	November	December
Habitats and vegetation	Recommended time to survey for mosses and lichens only		Recommended time to undertake Phase I habitat survey							Recommended time to survey for mosses and lichens only		
	Best time for planting and translocation		Planting and translocation of majority of species not recommended							Best time for planting and translocation		
Birds			Bird nesting season: no work if nesting birds found					Extended for some species				
	Vegetation clearance can take place but stop immediately if nesting birds are found								Vegetation clearance can take place but stop immediately if nesting birds are found			
Badgers	No work close to setts											No work close to setts
		Best time for field surveys									Best time for field surveys	
	Construction of artificial setts											Construction of artificial setts
			Territorial bait surveys can be done		Still OK for surveys, but they will not be as effective		Badger exclusion licensing season					
Bats	No work in hibernation roosts					No work in breeding roosts				No work in hibernation roosts		
Dormice	Good time to survey for nests as they are hibernating		If dormice are suspected stop work, report and put a protection plan into action						Good time to survey for nests as they are hibernating			
Red squirrels	If spotted, stop work as they are timid and extremely rare, so sighting needs to be reported											
			Breeding season, particularly vulnerable									
Water voles	Avoid all works in water vole habitat			Work in water vole habitat possible	Avoid all works in water vole habitat			Work in water vole habitat possible		Avoid all works in water vole habitat		

Figure 3.9.1: *Wildlife year planner*

Wildlife year planner – continued

Protected species	January	February	March	April	May	June	July	August	September	October	November	December
Reptiles	Avoid work	Avoid work		Best time for capture	Best time for capture			Best time for capture	Best time for capture		Avoid work	Avoid work
Great crested newts	No work in inhabited ponds	No work in inhabited ponds		Best time for terrestrial work	Best time for terrestrial work	Best time for licensing and surveying	Best time for licensing and surveying				No work in inhabited ponds	No work in inhabited ponds
Natterjack toads	Do not disturb Natterjack toad in hibernation	Do not disturb Natterjack toad in hibernation	Do not disturb Natterjack toad in hibernation / Best time for survey in ponds	Best time for survey in ponds	Best time for survey in ponds / Do not work in ponds with Natterjack toad or its spawn, do not move them without a licence	Do not work in ponds with Natterjack toad or its spawn, do not move them without a licence / Pond survey OK, but numbers considerably less	Do not work in ponds with Natterjack toad or its spawn, do not move them without a licence / Pond survey OK, but numbers considerably less	Surveys for adults on land	Surveys for adults on land	Do not disturb Natterjack toad in hibernation	Do not disturb Natterjack toad in hibernation	Do not disturb Natterjack toad in hibernation
Fish					Be aware this is the time for fish spawning and salmon runs – seek advice							

How to recognise problems

As always, the best thing to do is to prevent problems arising. However, the following indicate that there are serious problems on site:

- bats or other nocturnal animals being seen during daylight hours or found on the ground near to the site
- injured birds, smashed eggs, young unaccompanied fledglings
- dead fish floating in watercourse affected by works.

In December 2004 a construction contractor was fined £3000 after admitting that its work next to the River Mint in a Site of Special Scientific Interest (SSSI) had disturbed the ground of the riverbanks and bed. The contractor was also ordered to pay more than £4000 in legal costs to the Environment Agency, which brought the prosecution.

Unexpected ecological finds can arise during the works. The contractor has the responsibility to deal with these in the correct manner. This may affect the works.

Fines and costs for non-compliance

Disturbing protected species or damaging the places where they live can result in prosecution under a range of legislation. The fine for non-compliance with legislation varies according to the species and the type of damage caused. For example, if protected species such as bats, badgers, or great crested newts are disturbed, fines may be imposed at £5000 per animal. There is also scope for the confiscation of any vehicles or other equipment used to commit the offence.

Contract or planning conditions

Contract or planning conditions may state that certain trees must remain undamaged. Replacing damaged mature trees is expensive – a 10 m-high tree may cost £2000, plus extra expense for delivery, planting and several years maintenance.

Impact on project programme

In many cases, works have to be timed to avoid disturbance to species during particularly sensitive times, eg hibernation or mating seasons and the bird-nesting season. If this is not considered early enough in the project programme, disruption may be caused.

When damage has occurred, negotiating with the nature conservation bodies and repairing damage takes time and can cause delays to the programme.

Public awareness

Today the public is very aware of impacts on the natural environment and the damage that can be caused. Many projects are under the spotlight on environmental grounds and the public will notice poor environmental practice. Therefore, it is important for good public relations to have proper regard for ecological issues on site.

The nature conservation bodies

This term is used here to represent the following organisations that have regional responsibility for promoting the conservation of wildlife and natural features:

Conservation body	Contact number
Countryside Council for Wales	0845 1306 229
English Nature (Natural England from October 2006)	01733 455 000
Environment and Heritage Service Northern Ireland	028 90251477
Scottish Natural Heritage	0131 447 4784

Their remit includes providing ecological advice (such as consultation during planning), promoting biodiversity, protecting designated ecological sites, geological and geomorphological sites, and protected species. Within each area there are additional bodies that have an environmental remit, but no statutory process. These include county wildlife trusts and national and local environmental groups such as badger, bat and bird groups (eg the RSPB and WWF).

Main considerations

There are two ways in which ecological issues have to be considered on site.

1. **Where species or areas of the site have been identified for particular protection**

    In this instance, studies will have been carried out by an experienced consultant to determine the best way of dealing with them. Site staff should be made aware of the special working methods that they should follow to protect the species or area of site.

2. **Where protected species are discovered when the contractor is already on site and works have begun**

    Work should be stopped immediately, and the site manager should seek expert advice on how to proceed. Negotiations with the nature conservation bodies may then have to take place to discuss the best way forward.

To minimise general damage to ecology on site

Those working in construction should protect particular species and designated sites. It is important to take a responsible attitude to the natural environment as a whole. Be aware that most activities during construction can have a direct, temporary or permanent impact on the surrounding ecology, through such effects as:

- changes to water quality
- the destruction of places inhabited by plants and animals (this is a feature of most developments)
- interruptions to the movement of wildlife
- habitat fragmentation or vegetation damage
- removal of hedgerows and other vegetation
- high noise levels disturbing adjacent ecology
- changes in lighting
- damage, removal or burial of important rock formations or landforms.

Be aware that works on site may affect ecological resources off site.

How to avoid problems

The first step is to find out whether the client has identified any designated ecological sites or protected species – check that this information has been passed on to any contractors. Usually, particular working practices to protect the ecological features will have been recommended. Where these are given follow the advice. If no recommendations are given, seek advice from head office or the person assigned with environmental responsibility in the site environmental plan.

Before work begins, identify and fence off any sensitive habitats and restrict the movement of workers to designated areas. This will help to minimise the damage that may be caused. For many categories of wildlife, for example nesting birds and roosting bats, the timing of work will be important, so correct scheduling may avoid problems. Liaise with the nature conservation bodies and with local environmental groups for advice.

Dealing with key animals

Many animals, plants and birds are protected throughout or for part of the year under Schedule 5 of the **Wildlife and Countryside Act 1981 (as amended)**. Work may have to be adapted or delayed until such a time that the development will cause no adverse impact on them or the places where they live. Work may also be subject to licenses issued by the nature conservation bodies or Defra. These organisations should be consulted for advice.

Information about some of the key species that you may encounter is presented below.

Bats

Bats roost in a variety of localities in both urban and rural areas, these include:

- holes and cracks in trees
- in roofs and walls of buildings
- under bridges
- underground caves
- disused railway tunnels.

Bats hibernate between October and April and breed between May and September. If bats are likely to be encountered, a survey will be required by a licensed bat-worker to establish the location and size of the roost. It is only licensed bat-workers that are allowed legally to enter known bat roosts or to capture or handle bats. It is ILLEGAL to injure, kill, capture or disturb a bat, or to damage trees, buildings or other places used for roosting, even if the roost is currently unoccupied.

Badgers

Badgers and their setts are protected under the **Protection of Badgers Act 1992**. It is an offence to directly disturb a badger sett, or to carry out works close to a badger sett, which could cause a disturbance without a licence from the relevant nature conservation body or consent from Defra.

Badgers are widespread throughout the UK and can be found living in:

- woodland
- road and railway embankments
- refuse tips
- under buildings
- in hollow trees.

Setts are a network of tunnels and chambers underground, the entrance to which is visible above ground and can be identified by a rounded or flattened, oval-shaped hole and the presence of large spoil mounds.

Figure 3.9.2: *Man-made badger sett – Morrison*

A licence must be obtained for the following activities around active badger setts:

- use of heavy machinery within 30 m
- light machinery within 20 m
- use of hand tools within 10 m.

If a badger or a sett is discovered after works have started, work must STOP immediately and seek expert advice.

Foxes

Foxes occur in nearly all habitats and are well adapted to living in built-up areas, often being seen in town centres and gardens. Foxes are active all year round (less so during winter) and can be seen at any time of the day. Breeding occurs during spring. Foxes occupy underground dens called "earths". Be aware that a licence is required to damage badger setts even if occupied by foxes.

Cruelty to and trapping of foxes is ILLEGAL. Fox earths should not be destroyed until it is certain that they are unoccupied. Holes should not be filled between March and May, as cubs are likely to be below ground. If a fox earth is discovered after works have started, work must STOP immediately and expert advice sought.

Water voles

Water voles often are confused with rats. They can be found in burrows 2 m from the water edge near or below the water line in various localities:

- slow-flowing rivers
- streams
- ditches
- dykes
- around ponds and lakes.

Water voles tend to be more active during the day and are active all year round, but less so in winter. Water voles and their burrows are legally protected against damage and disturbance. If water voles are found after works have started, all works must STOP immediately to avoid breaking the law, and expert advice should be sought.

Reptiles

Remember that all reptiles are protected and should not be killed or injured. In the UK there are six native species of land-dwelling reptiles:

- common lizard
- sand lizard
- slow-worm
- adder
- grass snake
- smooth snake.

Reptiles hibernate in winter but are active the rest of the year. Mating takes place between April and June and the young are born between July and October. Reptiles can be found throughout the UK and are typically found in dense grassland, or scrub with open areas where they can bask, among vegetation on railway embankments and hedgerows. They can also be found sheltering under rocks and logs. It is ILLEGAL to kill or injure common lizards, slow-worms, grass snakes and adders. Works affecting sand lizards and smooth snakes are illegal without a licence. If reptiles are found, or are likely to be found, STOP work immediately and seek advice from an expert.

Amphibians

Great crested newts and natterjack toads are fully protected by law. Natterjack toads are extremely rare in Britain and unlikely to be found on site. To kill, injure, disturb them or their habitat, is an offence. If found or suspected on site all works must STOP immediately and expert advice sought.

Great crested newts can be found predominantly in ponds in rural, urban and suburban areas. Great crested newts are nocturnal and spend most of their time within grass, scrub, woodland and under logs within 500 m of a water body. They spawn in the ponds between March and June.

Nesting birds

All birds and their nests are protected under Schedule 1 of the **Wildlife and Countryside Act 1981** (and amendments), with some rare species, eg barn owl, birds of prey and kingfishers, carrying further protection against disturbance. The programming of tree and hedge removal should fall outside of the nesting season (March – end July).

Birds can be found nesting in unusual places on site, including on scaffolding or machinery, if this occurs the equipment cannot be used until the birds have finished nesting and the area may need to be sealed off to prevent disturbance. Consult the nature conservation bodies for further advice.

If you suspect that a protected plant or animal may be affected by your operations, **stop** and **seek** specialist advice before continuing.

To obtain a full list of species protected under the **Wildlife and Countryside Act 1981 (as amended)** contact the relevant nature conservation body and refer to the list on the accompanying CD. To assist dealing with them on site refer to CIRIA publications *Working with wildlife resource and training pack* and *Working with wildlife pocket book* (C587 and C613 respectively).

Noxious and invasive plants

Ecology is adversely affected through the spreading of noxious and invasive plants, and it is an offence to cause their spread. These plants are covered by Schedule 9 of the **Wildlife and Countryside Act 1981 (as amended)** or under the **Weeds Act 1959 (as amended)**:

- Japanese knotweed (grows densely, shades out other plants, reduces biodiversity, penetrates asphalt, walls, and foundations)
- Giant hogweed (poisonous sap)
- Ragwort (poisonous to sheep, horses, etc)
- Thistle (shades out other plants, reduces biodiversity)
- Himalayan balsam (grows densely, shades out other plants, and reduces biodiversity).

Figure 3.9.3: *Japanese knotweed plant*

It can be very expensive to remove Japanese knotweed through removal and disposal of surrounding soil 7 m around the plant and to a depth of 3.5 m.

If you come across noxious or invasive plants on site it is your responsibility to take the following action:

- cordon off the area to prevent any inadvertent spreading
- notify environmental regulator that plant is present
- ensure any vehicles that have been in the affected area have their wheels/tracks thoroughly washed before leaving the site
- spray with herbicide to kill off top growth and commence root killing
- excavate main stump and put in skip to dry before licensed burning and disposal to landfill
- excavate all traces of root under controlled conditions – spreading of spoil on polythene on open area of site
- spray with herbicide of all new growth on spoil area over two-year period
- incorporate "clean spoil" into landscaping.

Animal pests

Pigeons

Pigeons are widespread and can be found in many places, particularly urban areas. Roosting and nesting sites are aesthetically annoying, and can transmit disease in an enclosed area. The material left behind, both in active and abandoned roosts, is hazardous to health and must be disposed of carefully to prevent risks to health and contamination of soil.

Rats

Rats can cause problems by gnawing on woodwork, water pipes and electric cables. They can be found in gaps under sheds, loose piles of rubbish and building materials. There are three main strategies to deal with and deter rats:

1. Rat-proofing – filling holes, fixing metal collars around pipes, using metal sheet guards and covering areas that need to be open with galvanised mesh, adding pathways and stretches of lawn.

2. Trapping – mechanical traps set before rat-proofing.

3. Chemical control – commonly using anti-coagulants rodenticides (eg Warfarin). The use of rodenticides should be undertaken only by specialised contractors, as these are extremely hazardous to *all* mammals.

Habitats

Habitat can be defined as an area possessing uniformity of land form, vegetation, climate or any other quality assumed to be important. Usually, in terms of site assessment and management, it is uniformity of vegetation that characterises a habitat. Habitats are either created naturally or man-made through translocation (see next page). There are a number of types of habitat:

- coastal and marine
- grassland
- heathland
- hedgerows and individual trees
- road and railway embankments
- soil
- urban areas
- wetland
- woodland and scrub.

The ecological richness of a habitat (its biodiversity) can be affected in a number of ways. Invasive plants such as Japanese knotweed can reduce biodiversity through out-competing other plant species. Human impacts include spillages of hazardous substances on the ground and into water, felling trees, removing hedgerows and disturbing badger setts, etc.

Measures to reinstate habitats damaged during the works may form part of the contract or planning conditions. Such measures have to be planned in advance and may require specialist advice. There may be particular requirements in selecting the type of species for reinstating.

Translocation of species

Translocation is when habitat damage is anticipated and unavoidable, and species are moved off the site. Translocation forms part of the site preparation works and is carried out by specialists within specific time periods (refer to Figure 3.9.1), and may influence the project programme. Both aftercare and monitoring of translocated species are essential. Various Acts concerning animal welfare legislation may apply (for example, the **Protection of Animals Act 1911** and the **Wild Mammals (Protection) Act 1996**). Without prior planning and consideration, translocation may become a very expensive process. Refer to CIRIA's *Habitat translocation – a best practice guide* (C600) and *A review of habitat translocation* (C601) for further details.

Natural features

Designated sites

Sites with important ecological attributes (both plant and animal species) or natural landforms can be given special protection that can be applied at the regional, national or international level according to their importance, rarity or typicalness. Examples of designated sites are:

- Area of Outstanding Natural Beauty (AONB)
- County Wildlife Sites (CWS)
- Local Nature Reserve (LNR)
- National Nature Reserve (NNR)
- Special Area of Conservation (SAC)
- Special Protection Area (SPA)
- Sites of Importance for Nature Conservation (SINC's)
- Sites of Nature Conservation Interest (SNCI's)

- Site of Special Scientific Interest (SSSI) or Area of Special Scientific Interest (ASSI)
- RAMSAR (Wetlands of international importance)
- Regionally important Geological Sites (RIGS)
- World Heritage Sites.

Always contact the nature conservation body for further guidance on designated sites.

It is an offence to carry out works on a designated site without the permission of the nature conservation bodies. They usually require several months' notice before works begin. It is important to adhere to working methods once they have been agreed with the nature conservation bodies.

Trees and hedgerows

Damage to trees and hedgerows may be caused either through direct physical injury to the branches, trunk or roots or by changing the soil character around the roots. This can arise from various actions including compaction (even one piece of machinery going over the roots can cause damage), raising soil levels, impervious covering around tree roots, raising the water table, hazardous spillages, soil stripping, or excavations. Refer to the checklist at the end of this Section for more details.

Tree protection

A tree preservation order (TPO) protects a single tree, group of trees or woodland. It protects trees from being topped, lopped or removed. Consent must be obtained before any work on a tree with a TPO is undertaken. Failure to gain permission is an offence and could result in a fine of up to £20 000. All trees located within a conservation area are protected.

The local authority planning department should be contacted before you work on any protected trees. The procedure to gain permission to work on a tree(s) with a TPO on it are:

- obtain the relevant form from the local authority
- fill out the form outlining the intended work
- return the completed form to the local authority
- the local authority has up to two months to make a decision (local residents are able to appeal against the work during this time).

When a tree that has a TPO in force is dead, dying or dangerous, it can be felled without permission, but the local authority should always be consulted before any action is taken.

Before removing any trees on local authority land, the relevant authority needs to be contacted. It can then place a provisional TPO on any tree(s) under threat of damage or removal from construction works.

Hedgerow protection

Hedgerows are protected under the **1997 Hedgerow Regulations,** which make it a legal requirement to notify your district or borough council before removing a hedgerow or part thereof. Under regulations the removal of any hedge longer then 20 m, requires planning permission. If the hedge is shown to be significant in terms of its age, environmental or historical importance, then the planning authority can refuse such permission (after a six-week determination period) and take further measures to protect the hedgerow.

Rocks and landforms

These are an important part of our natural heritage. Some rock exposures and landforms will be SSSIs/ASSIs but others may be locally important. If you are in doubt as to the importance of these features and how to protect them, contact the nature conservation bodies who will give you contact details for your local RIGS group.

Wildlife and natural features 3.9

Checklists – Wildlife and natural features

What to look out for on site	
Nesting birds ■ if found, do not disturb or cut down trees or shrubs – to avoid accidental disturbance do not fell or clear any trees or shrubs between March and July	
Trees ■ check whether any trees on site are covered by a tree preservation order and liaise with local authority (local planning office in Northern Ireland)	

Working near water	
Place a protective bund around ponds to prevent water pollution	
Dewatering can affect the ecology of wetlands around the site. Consider monitoring water levels during the works	

Avoiding damage to trees and hedgerows	
Keep vehicles and plant away from them	
Put up temporary fencing to mark out this area	
Do not cut or damage any roots greater than 25 mm in diameter within the protected area	
Cut roots only with a clean hand saw, not a spade or mechanical digger	
Wrap damp sacking around any exposed roots until ready for backfilling	
Backfill holes with care, to ensure that roots are not damaged, and compact backfill lightly	
Do not store spoil or building materials within protected area or under tree canopy	
Keep toxic materials such as diesel and cement well away	
Always avoid damaging bark or branches	

Regulatory

PPG 5 (See Appendix 1)

Protected species

Bat mitigation guidelines, English Nature, 2004
Great crested newts – guidelines for developers, English Nature
Badgers – guidelines for developers, English Nature, 1995
Badgers and development, EHS, Natural Heritage, 2004
Reptiles: a guide for developers, English Nature, 2004
Working with wildlife. A resource and training pack for the construction industry, CIRIA C587
Working with wildlife pocket book, CIRIA C613
The new rivers and wildlife handbook, The Royal Society for the Protection of Birds, 1994.

Habitats

Habitat translocation – a best practice guide, CIRIA C600
A review of habitat translocation, CIRIA C601.

Legislation

A brief summary and interpretation of the legislation relevant to construction activities can be found free of charge on the Internet at www.netregs.org

Additionally **CIRIA** has produced supporting good practice advice which is available free of charge at www.ciria.org/complianceplus

Wildlife and Countryside Act 1981 (and amendments)

This legislation covers SSSIs, SPAs and RAMSAR sites. It also covers several hundred plant and animal species under various different schedules:

- Schedule 1 – birds
- Schedule 5 – animals
- Schedule 8 – plants
- Schedule 9 – invasive plants.

Conservation (Natural Habitats, &c) Regulations 1994 (The Habitats Regulations)

Allows for the designation of SACs, and SPAs, collectively known as "European Sites". All the protected species listed on the schedules of the Regulations are also listed within the **Wildlife and Countryside Act 1981 (and amendments)**.

Protection of Badgers Act 1992

Aims to protect the welfare of badgers rather than conservation. The badger was too common to be included in the Wildlife and Countryside Act 1981.

Environmental Protection Act 1990

Places a duty of care on all waste producers. It concerns the procedure that needs to be followed when disposing of invasive plants.

Hedgerow Regulations 1997

Makes it illegal to remove a protected hedge without permission from the local authority.

Town & Country Planning (Trees) Regulations 1999

Provides the power to protect specified trees and woodlands through the serving of tree preservation orders (TPOs).

Countryside and Rights of Way Act 2000

Part III revises the site protection provisions of the **Wildlife and Countryside Act 1981** and provides legal mechanisms aimed at achieving more positive management of SSSIs and other designated sites including AONBs, and RAMSAR sites.

Weed Act 1959 (as amended)

Requires the occupiers of land on which injurious weeds are growing to take action to prevent the spread of injurious weeds. The Act specifies five such species: Common Ragwort, Spear Thistle, Creeping Field Thistle, Broad leaved Dock and Curled Dock.

Applicable legislation in Northern Ireland

- Wildlife Order (NI), 1985 similar to the Wildlife and Countryside Act 1981 (and amendments)

- The Conservation (Natural Habitats) Regulations NI, 1995 similar to the Conservation (Natural Habitats, &c.) Regulations 1994 (The Habitats Regulations)

- Environment Order NI, 2002

- Noxious Weeds (Northern Ireland) Order 1977 (details on DARD's website) similar to the Weeds Act 1959 (as amended).

Construction process 4

4.1 Introduction

At every stage of the construction process there is the potential for environmental problems to arise. This Section identifies some of the key issues that may occur during a range of processes and refers you to relevant sections within this handbook for guidance.

4.2 Bored tunnelling

Key issues	Refer to
Impacts on groundwater, which could have subsequent impacts on ecological habitats	3.8, 3.9
Disposal of spoil and slurry arising from tunnelling works and traffic impacts associated with long distance transport	3.7, 3.6
Buildings sensitive to ground-borne vibration in the locality of planned ground level tunnels	3.5
24-hour working causing annoyance to neighbours near the tunnel portal	2.3.1, 3.5
Encountering contaminated ground or groundwater during tunnelling. Follow the steps below if encountered: ▪ stop work immediately ▪ report the discovery to the site manager who must seek expert advice ▪ seal off the area to contain spread of contaminants ▪ clear site to ensure there is nothing that could cause fire or explosion ▪ contact the regulator or local authority once it is confirmed that contamination is found ▪ ensure that the suspected contamination is tested and characterised and agree changes to the existing remedial plan ▪ follow good practice guidance to remediate the land	3.4, 3.8, 3.7
Discovery of archaeological finds (including old cemeteries)	3.1
Subsidence caused in listed building in locality of tunnel portal	3.5, 3.1

4.3 Brick/blockwork

Key issues	Refer to
Unnecessary wastage of materials by: ▪ not over-ordering materials ▪ storing in packaging to protect them ▪ storing away from vehicle movements ▪ preventing ready-mixed mortar from drying out ▪ avoiding cutting and chasing	3.7, 3.2
Reuse of excess bricks or blocks, either on or off site. If damaged use them as hardcore on site access roads	3.7
Segregation and recycling of packaging wastes	3.2, 3.7
Dust nuisance from cutting and chasing	3.7

4   Construction process

4.4   Concrete batching

Key issues	Refer to
Minimising visual, noise and dust disturbance to neighbours. Plant likely to require authorisation under the **Environmental Protection Act 1990**	2.3.1, 3.5, 3.3
Annoyance to neighbours from noise of motors and conveyors	3.5
Minimising wastage and contamination of aggregates during storage	3.7, 3.2
Storage and disposal of additives to prevent spillage and contamination	3.7, 4.20
Surface drainage from the area around the batching plant may be polluted, so consents required to store and dispose	3.8, 3.7
Accurate prediction of volume required to avoid over production and wastage	3.7, 3.2
Potential of highly alkaline washout from mixing plant or cleaning of ready-mix concrete lorries contaminating watercourses	3.8
Release of concrete from concreting operations that are near or in watercourses (floating batchers)	3.8, 4.22
Recycling of returned concrete to reduce washout volumes and produce viable aggregate	3.2, 3.7
Potential of alkaline cement dust released from silos during filling to harm ecology and annoy neighbours	3.9, 3.3
When cleaning silos, reverse jet filters will minimise dust emissions by capturing and reusing cement dust	3.3
Prevention of overfilling and spillage from pipelines and pumps because of poor maintenance	2.4, 4.14
Maintain plant well to prevent noise and emissions	4.14, 3.5

4.5 Concrete pours and aftercare

Key issues	Refer to
Control the storage, handling and disposal of shutter oils	3.2, 4.20
Blowing dust and debris out of formwork can annoy neighbours. Consider suction	2.3.1, 3.3
Consider the wastes that will be generated and plan their handling and disposal. For example: concrete curing compounds (spray applications), blackjack waterproofing (silane), PVC sheeting, frost protection materials	3.7
A concrete pour may displace wastewaters from the hole. These may be contaminated with sediment and cleaning materials from the side of the structure. Dispose of them appropriately	3.8, 3.7
In or near a watercourse, control the placing of any wet concrete to minimise the risk of cement leaking into the watercourse. Shutter failure in such locations can cause major pollution in the watercourse	4.22, 3.8
The washout from concrete mixing plant, or and from the cleaning of ready-mix concrete lorries, is contaminated with cement and so is highly alkaline. Do not allow it to enter any watercourse	3.8
To reuse washout water obtain consent and dispose of it to the foul sewer via a settling tank	3.8
Large areas of concrete can create dust when dry, so sweep regularly	3.3

4.6 Crushing, screening and reuse of materials

Key issues	Refer to
Under the **Environmental Protection Act 1990** authorisation will be needed to operate a crusher and screener on site	2.3.1
Ensure you work within the requirements of your consent in terms of emissions, working hours and monitoring regime	2.3.1, 3.3
When operating a crusher ensure it is sited away from sensitive receptors	3.5
Ensure screens are erected around the crusher to minimise impacts of noise and dust	3.5, 3.3
Stockpiled material should be suitably covered to prevent dust arising	3.3
Implement a traffic management plan to manage traffic in and around the site	3.6
Ensure effective use of crushed and screened materials on site	3.2, 3.7

4.7   Demolition

Key issues	Refer to
Locate and mark all underground pipes, tanks and services. Also label all tanks with their content and capacity. Check for any visible signs of leaking tanks or pipes, and any signs of contaminated ground or groundwater	3.8, 3.4
Before demolition begins, review the disposal options for the materials that will be generated. Reclaim and reuse materials where possible. Identify markets for materials. Segregate materials as they are generated. Label waste clearly and store in a designated area. Dispose of any materials in accordance with your duty of care	3.2, 3.7
If materials like concrete or masonry are to be crushed on site, check that you have obtained any necessary licences from the local environmental health officer in England, Wales and Northern Ireland or SEPA in Scotland, (process authorisation under the **Environmental Protection Act 1990**)	3.3, 3.5
Before removing or perforating tanks, check that all of their contents and residues have been emptied for safe disposal by a competent operator. Pipes may contain significant quantities of oil or chemicals, and should be capped, or valves closed, to prevent spillage. Ensure that suitable spill response materials and emergency instructions are available on site and that staff have been adequately trained	3.8, 3.7, 2.4
Noise and vibration may annoy neighbours. Consider screening the works	3.5, 2.3.1
Dust from the demolition process may annoy neighbours and damage ecology near the site. Damp down structures during demolition. Ensure that any runoff from the site is prevented from entering watercourses or soakaways	3.3, 3.8
If elephant chutes are being used, ensure that each section is securely fixed, that the skip or lorry at the discharge end is covered, and that materials are dampened before being sent down the chute	3.3
Prevent dust escaping from materials in lorries leaving the site. If it is not possible to cover lorries because there are pieces of protruding material, spray them with water just before they leave	3.3

Construction process 4

4.8 Dredging

Key issues	Refer to
Dredgings may be contaminated with substances such as oils and heavy metals; sample and test the sediments to provide vital information for considering disposal options. Aim to reuse the dredgings (for example, to improve agricultural land) rather than disposing of them to landfill	3.8, 3.7
Plan the disposal of dredgings before starting works, to allow time for obtaining any permissions required under **Waste Management Licensing Regulations 1994**	3.8
Disposing of dredgings at sea requires a licence. It can take up to three months to obtain a licence for a new site	Defra
Dredging materials contaminated with heavy metals or oils may lead to the production of materials classified as hazardous waste, and as such appropriate disposal will be required	3.7
If landfilling the dredgings, obtain an exemption from landfill tax for dredgings arising from maintenance of navigable inland waterways	3.7
Obtain a discharge consent for returning effluent from dewatering dredgings to controlled waters	3.8
The dewatering sediments may give rise to an odour problem	3.3
Dredging may affect the aquatic ecology. Use an appropriate dredging technique (eg dredge mats and silt curtains) to minimise the disturbance of sediment resulting in silting of the watercourse and potential mobilisation of contaminants	3.8
Disturbance of organic silts and dying weed may give rise to deoxygenation. Monitor and aerate if necessary	3.8
Working with compacted sediments may generate high levels of noise. Also, mechanical dewatering and compaction may lead to vibration	3.5

4   Construction process

4.9   Earthworks

Key issues	Refer to
Minimise the surplus materials arising from earthworks by considering methods of improving the spoil (eg *in-situ* stabilisation)	3.2, 3.7, 3.4
Dispose of surplus materials arising from earthworks in accordance with **Environmental Protection (Duty of Care) Regulations, 1991.** Testing of the spoil may be required to provide information for considering disposal options. Aim to reuse spoil (eg for land profiling and raising) rather than disposing of it to landfill	3.7
Be aware that above 90 cubic metres, a waste management licence will be required to store arisings on site in accordance with the **Waste Management Licensing Regulations 1994**	3.7, 3.2
Be aware of unexpected contamination revealed during earthworks. Halt works immediately, clear the site and seek expert advice	3.4, 3.8
Be aware of unexpected archaeological finds. Materials to look out for during excavations include: burned or blackened material, brick or tile fragments, coins, pottery or bone fragments, skeletons, timber joints or post holes, brick or stone foundations, infilled ditches	3.1
Be aware of unexpected ecological finds, for example the presence of newts. Should you discover any species stop work immediately and seek expert advice	3.9
Surface water management. Keep water off unsurfaced areas using measures such as cut-off drains. Control and dispose of silty water properly	3.8
Earthmoving plant and vehicles used to transport materials from and around the site may cause impacts from emissions, mud and noise. Construct appropriate haul roads. Maintain plant and vehicles. Use a wheel wash to minimise dirt on roads	3.6, 3.5, 3.3, 3.8, 4.14, 4.20

4.10 Excavation

Key issues	Refer to
Excavations within retained bases may be formed by sheet diaphragm walling or secant piling	4.13
Prevent water entering excavations. When water does enter excavations, take measures to avoid it becoming contaminated. Dispose of it properly	3.8, 3.7
Be aware of unexpected archaeological finds. Materials to look out for during excavations include: burned or blackened material, brick or tile fragments, coins, pottery or bone fragments, skeletons, timber joints or post holes, brick or stone foundations, infilled ditches	3.1
If excavation reveals contamination, halt digging immediately. Clear the site immediately and where appropriate, try as far as possible to identify the extent and cause of contamination (eg spillage on site, rupture of subterranean pipeline) and attempt to contain contaminants. Seek expert advice	3.4, 3.8
If asbestos is uncovered unexpectedly during digging operations, halt digging operations at once and refill the excavation. Exposure of asbestos to the open air can result in widespread contamination as the particles are easily airborne far from site. Remove personnel immediately and secure the area. Contact site management immediately	3.7
Excavation plant and vehicles used to transport materials from and around the site may cause impacts from emissions, mud and noise. Poorly maintained plant and vehicles cause more environmental effects than well-maintained plant	3.3, 3.5, 3.8, 2.2.5, 4.14, 4.20
Use a wheel wash to minimise dirt on public highway	3.8
Spoil arising from excavation can be recycled if not contaminated. Crush any rock arising and use on or off site. Store topsoil for reuse in piles less than 2 metres high to prevent damage to the soil structure. Use excavated materials to form noise bunds and for landscaping – check whether planning permission is required	3.2, 3.5, 3.7

4.11 Grouting

Key issues	Refer to
Blowback from blockages or overfilling from pressure grouting with dry materials (eg cement) can cause significant dust problems. Working within an enclosure may be necessary in particularly sensitive areas	3.3
Grouting in or near contaminated ground may displace polluted water in the excavation. Prevent the uncontrolled release of this water	3.8, 3.4
Prevent the uncontrolled discharge of cements and bentonite slurries. Use a settlement tank to remove sediments and obtain a discharge consent before releasing the effluent	3.8
Grout waste can be more successfully separated by the addition of a chemical flocculant, or by hydroclone separation or mechanical dewatering. This allows easier disposal of the constituents	3.7, 3.8
Deal with any slurry waste (water mixed with silt) appropriately	3.8

4.12 Microtunnelling

Key issues	Refer to
Maintain small plant to minimise emissions	4.21, 4.14, 3.3
Properly manage wastes arising from the works	3.7
Noise from microtunnelling may annoy neighbours	3.5, 2.3.1
Traffic entering and leaving site may disrupt normal traffic flow. Emissions from traffic may annoy neighbours	3.6, 3.3, 3.5
Microtunnelling can damage tree roots	3.9
Contaminated ground may be encountered, which could introduce a pathway through which contaminants, mobilised by groundwater, may escape. Therefore, it is important to develop a contingency plan for dealing with it. If contaminated ground is encountered, halt works, clear the site, and seek expert advice	3.4, 3.8
Contaminated spoil should be stored separately from other materials and be disposed of according to **Hazardous Waste Regulations 2005**	3.7, 3.4

4.13 Piling

Key issues	Refer to
Consider using proprietary access track systems to minimise damage to tree roots and habitats	3.9
Maintain plant regularly to optimise fuel efficiency	4.14
Minimise the risk of spillage in using oils and chemicals	2.4, 4.20
Noise and vibration may annoy neighbours. The noise levels created by piling vary with the method used. Some methods will not be allowed in urban areas, or other sensitive locations where the site has immediate residential neighbours – so use the right plant	3.5
Manage bentonite appropriately to prevent its release to the environment. Recycle if possible or dispose of it properly	4.4, 4.5, 4.11, 3.7, 3.8
Manage wastes arising from the piling operations. Wastes from bored piling may be a particular problem as it is often wet. Dispose of this waste properly	3.7, 3.8
Piling close to watercourses forms a potential pollution risk	4.23, 4.22, 3.8
Contaminated ground may be encountered, which could introduce a pathway through which contaminants, mobilised by groundwater, may escape. Therefore, it is important to develop a contingency plan for dealing with it. If it is encountered, halt works, clear the site and seek expert advice	3.4, 3.9, 3.8
Contaminated spoil should be stored separately from other materials and be disposed of according to Hazardous Waste Regulations 2005	3.7

4.14 Plant maintenance

Key issues	Refer to
Designate an area within the site compound for routine plant maintenance	3.8
Surface water runoff from plant maintenance may contain pollutants (eg oils). Prevent their release to controlled waters	3.8
Ensure that appropriately trained personnel carry out repairs to plant	
Develop a protocol for disposing of wastes from maintenance	3.7
Dispose of old filters carefully as they contain substantial quantities of oil; some engine oils are hazardous wastes	3.7
Encourage the use of biodegradable oil substitutes over non-biodegradable	3.2
Recycle used oils	3.2
Tyres cannot be sent to landfill, therefore find appropriate route for recycling them	3.7
Prepare for spillages. Display the site's emergency response procedure at the plant maintenance area. Ensure a spillage kit is kept there and that all personnel know how to use it. Carry a spill kit in all repair vehicles	2.4, 3.8
Check replacement periods for hydraulic pipework and carry out regular checks. Use biodegradable oil for hydraulics. Blowouts regularly cause pollution incidents	3.2, 3.6
Check other pipework for signs of leaks. Prevent plant from dripping oil on the ground and polluting it	3.2, 3.6
Try to minimise the amount of refuelling or maintenance that occurs outside the designated area	4.20, 3.2
Install drip trays on plant where possible. Ensure that these are emptied regularly	
Store hazardous materials carefully to minimise the risk of spillage	2.2.4, 4.20, 3.2

4.15 Refurbishment of buildings

Key issues	Refer to
Explore the opportunities for reusing and recycling materials in the refurbishment. These materials may have arisen as waste on site or may originate off site	3.2, 3.7
There is a risk of exposing asbestos during the works, for example, by drilling into walls and ceilings. Ask the building owner and/or manager for detailed information on the location of asbestos in the building. Seek advice on what action to take if asbestos is uncovered	3.7
Any wastes arising from the works must be handled appropriately and disposed of in accordance with legislation	3.7
Noise and vibration from works may annoy the building's inhabitants	3.5

4   Construction process

4.16 Repairs to exposed structural elements
(eg bridge soffits, cladding)

Key issues	Refer to
Prevent debris from works falling onto the ground or water below. This should be incorporated into the working methods. It is especially important for works over public areas or near watercourses and sensitive ecological sites	3.8, 3.9, 4.22
Store hazardous materials carefully to minimise the risk of spillage	2.2.4, 4.20, 3.2
Noise from the works may annoy neighbours	3.5, 2.3.1
Carrying out repairs over a watercourse has potential to pollute it	3.8, 3.9, 4.22

4.17 Roadworks

Key issues	Refer to
Minimise the risk of spillage in using oils, bitumens and chemicals	2.4, 4.20
Noise and vibration may annoy neighbours. Night time working may cause additional annoyance	3.5, 2.3.1
Traffic entering and leaving the site may disrupt normal traffic flow. Emissions from traffic may annoy neighbours	3.3, 3.6
Much of the waste material arising from roadworks can be recycled	3.7
Do not discharge gully pot residues to underground or surface waters. Alternative disposal options include discharging to the foul sewer (with the consent of the local sewerage provider) after solids settlement, or at a suitably licensed waste disposal site	3.8

4.18 Site clearance

Key issues	Refer to
Follow contingency plan if contaminated land is discovered	3.5
Discovery and relocation of protected species (wildlife and/and or vegetation)	3.9
Effects on local ecological habitats by altering ground conditions (eg disturbance of badger setts)	3.9
Removal and reinstatement of vegetation (habitat translocation)	3.9
Archaeological finds (including human remains)	3.1
Noise, dust and vibration created during operations (eg movement of materials around site)	3.3, 3.5
Pollution of site water supply or nearby watercourses	3.8
Reuse of materials where possible (eg brickwork for hardcore)	3.2, 3.7
Waste disposal in accordance with regulations (eg waste carrier's licence)	3.7

4.19 Temporary works

Key issues	Refer to
Ensure that required permissions have been sought before any works begin. For example Section 61 consent from the local authority	3.5
Take care when carrying out temporary works near watercourses	3.8, 4.22
On-site fabrication of steelwork may be noisy and annoy neighbours	3.5, 2.3.1
Reuse materials on site or off site	3.7, 3.2

4.20 Use of oils and chemicals

Key issues	Refer to
COSHH assessments need to be held on site for any potentially hazardous materials. These provide advice on the type of storage needed for the chemicals, ie bunded areas, storage of flammable products in locked cupboards	3.4, 3.8, 3.2
Proper storage of hazardous materials reduces wastage and reduces the risk of spillages that could result in possible ground or groundwater contamination	3.2, 3.7
Oil storage should be in accordance with **Control of Pollution (Oil Storage) (England) Regulations 2001**. Similar regulations have been consulted upon by the Scottish Executive for application in Scotland though at the time of this document going to print Scottish regulations remain to be enacted. These regulations do not apply in Northern Ireland and Wales, but consideration should be taken to meet the requirements, as they are designed to prevent contamination of the water environment which would be an offence under other legislation	3.2
Transfer chemicals between containers only within a suitably bunded area. Spillages outside this area could result in ground or water contamination	3.7. 3.8
When using fuel, follow the refuelling protocol to minimise the risk of spillage	3.2
Minimise accidental spillages and have emergency procedures in place in case of a spill. Ensure there is a spill kit available and personnel are trained to use it	2.4, 3.8
Any disposal of product or empty product containers should be in accordance with waste management legislation and the related COSHH datasheet	3.2. 3.7

4.21 Use of small plant

Key issues	Refer to
Develop a refuelling protocol for your site and follow it	3.2
Maintain plant regularly to optimise fuel efficiency and prevent pollution incidents	4.14
Prevent water pollution and ground contamination. Use drip trays under stationary plant to contain oil leaks	4.20, 3.8, 3.4
Ensure that only trained personnel use plant and that they use it for its intended purpose	
Remember that water containing oils or other chemical contamination cannot be discharged to watercourses or on to the ground	3.8
Secure plant from vandals, as they cause pollution incidents	2.3.3
Noise and vibration from plant (eg generators and poker vibrators) may annoy neighbours and disturb ecology. Where possible, use quiet plant	3.5, 3.9

Construction process 4

4.22 Working near water

Key issues	Refer to
Check that permission has been obtained for any temporary works	3.8, 4.19
Special consideration needs to be taken when working on pontoons and barges	3.9
Supervise closely all plant refuelling. Fill portable fuel tanks and spare fuel containers away from the water's edge and never overfill	3.2, 4.20
Keep adequate supplies of booms and oil absorbent material available at all times for emergency use in case of a spillage. Dispose of any used absorbents in accordance with Duty of Care	2.4, 3.8, 3.7
Prevent pollution from plant used near a watercourse. Maintain plant regularly. Use drip trays	4.14
Ensure that the runoff from haul roads near or over watercourses cannot enter the watercourse	3.8
Erect temporary haul road bridges to prevent pollution and damage to stream beds	3.8
Where watercourse embankments are stripped of vegetation, stabilise them to prevent erosion. This may be done by seeding them using clover or fast growing grasses and covering with biodegradable sheeting	3.8, 3.2
Prevent dust or litter blowing into watercourses	3.3, 3.8
Be aware of potential direct or indirect disturbance to the bankside and in-stream ecology	3.9
Ensure that works are secured from vandals.	2.3.3

4 Construction process

4.23 Working with groundwater

Key issues	Refer to
Notify the environmental regulator where extensive dewatering is to occur so they may issue a conservation notice	3.8
Any groundwater abstracted from site needs to be disposed of. Generally the best environmental option is to return it to groundwater. Seek advice from the environmental regulator before implementing this solution as discharge consent may be required	3.8
There is a risk of mobilising ground contamination when working with groundwater and a potential risk of ground instability. If any contamination is suspected, seek specialist advice before proceeding	3.4
Consider monitoring for petrol/oil or diesel compounds that will float on the groundwater surface and move with the flow of water	3.4, 3.8
Works affecting groundwater may have an impact on adjacent ecology. Seek specialist ecological advice before any works are carried out	3.9, 3.8
Dewatering may cause a change in groundwater levels and affect river/stream flows. A solution is to monitor water levels in sensitive areas and recharge with the extracted groundwater of the correct quality and temperature	3.8
Minimise the risk of spillage when using oils and chemicals	2.4, 4.20

UK environmental regulators and heritage bodies

Regulator	Responsibilities	Contact number	Website
Environment Agency – England and Wales	Discharges to land and controlled water, waste, effluent discharges, abstraction licences some nature conservation functions, ground contamination, enforcing environmental legislation	08708 506 506	www.environment-agency.gov.uk
Scottish Environment Protection Agency (SEPA)	Discharges to land and controlled water, waste, some nature conservation functions, ground contamination and water abstraction	01786 457 700	www.sepa.org.uk
Environment and Heritage Service Northern Ireland (EHSNI)	Discharges to land and controlled water, waste, nature conservation functions, ground contamination and the built heritage	028 9025 1477	www.ehsni.gov.uk
Department of Environment Food and Rural Affairs (Defra)	Policy maker for all aspects of the environment, rural matters, farming and food production at national level	08459 33 55 77	www.defra.gov.uk
Local authority	Noise, air quality, traffic, the planning process and contaminated land. Some powers under waste legislation to stop, search waste carriers and confiscate vehicles		www.open.gov.uk

Appendix

UK environmental regulators and heritage bodies (cont)

Regulator	Responsibilities	Contact number	Website
English Nature (Natural England from October 2006)	Designated ecological sites, geological and geomorphological sites, and protected species	01733 455 000	www.english-nature.org.uk
Countryside Council for Wales	National wildlife conservation authority and adviser on sustaining natural beauty	0845 1306 229	www.ccw.gov.uk
Cadw	Designated archaeological and heritage sites in Wales	01443 336 000	www.cadw.wales.gov.uk
English Heritage	Responsible for protecting historic buildings, landscapes and archaeological sites	0870 333 1181	www.english-heritage.org.uk
Scottish Natural Heritage	Designated ecological sites, geological and geomorphological sites, and protected species	0131 447 4784	www.snh.org.uk
Historic Scotland (agency within Scottish Executive)	Safeguarding the nation's built heritage	0131 668 8600	www.historic-scotland.gov.uk

Appendix 2

Useful contacts

Organisation	Background	Contact number	Website
Chartered Institute of Environmental Health	Maintains, enhances and promotes improvements in public and environmental health	020 7928 6006	www.cieh.org
CIRIA	Construction-specific research, implementation and publications, produced collaboratively with the industry	020 7549 3300	www.ciria.org
Considerate Constructors Scheme	Voluntary code of practice for the construction industry	0800 783 1423	www.ccscheme.org.uk
Envirowise	Runs waste minimisation clubs; provides free information helpline, case studies and good-practice guides	0800 585 794	www.envirowise.gov.uk
Health & Safety Executive	Advice on health and safety issues	08701 545 500	www.hse.gov.uk
National Trust	Responsible for protecting historic buildings, landscapes and archaeological sites	0870 609 5380	www.nationaltrust.org.uk
National Trust for Scotland	Responsible for protecting historic buildings, landscapes and archaeological sites	0131 243 9300	www.nts.org.uk
NetRegs	Web site run by Environment Agency detailing industry sector legislation		www.netregs.org

3 Appendix

Regulatory Pollution Prevention Guidance notes

The table below lists the Pollution Prevention Guidance (PPG) notes that have been produced by the environmental regulators and that have been highlighted as key guidance for topics discussed within this guide.

Single copies of the PPG notes outlined below are available free of charge (only for the first copy), from the environmental regulators or can be downloaded from the Environment Agency website at www.environment-agency.gov.uk/ppg or by phoning 08708 506 506.

PPG	Title	Relevant topics
1	General guide to the prevention of pollution	3.8
2	Above ground oil storage tanks	3.2, 3.8
3	Use and design of oil separators in surface water drainage systems	3.8
4	Disposal of Sewage where no mains drainage is available	3.8
5	Works in, near or liable to affect watercourses	3.8, 3.9
6	Working at construction and demolition sites	3.8
7	Refuelling facilities	3.8
8	Safe storage and disposal of used oils	3.8
18	The control of spillages and fire fighting run-off	3.8
21	Pollution incident response planning	2.4, 3.8
23	Maintenance of structures over water	3.8
26	Storage and handling of drums and intermediate bulk containers	3.2
27	Installation, decommissioning and removal of underground storage tanks	3.8

Details of the further PPG's are also available from the Environment Agency website.

CIRIA C650

Other CIRIA guidance

Site guides	Code
Coastal and marine environmental site guide	C584
Working with wildlife pocket book	C613
Site health handbook	C629
Waste minimisation in construction – site guide	SP133
Site safety handbook (third edition)	SP151
The essential green guide	SP158
Training	
Environmental good practice on site – training pack	C525
Waste minimisation in construction – training pack and revised guide	C555
Environmental performance improvement clubs (CD)	C585
Working with wildlife resource and training pack for the construction industry	C587
Implementation of remedial options for contaminated land – training pack	C612
The observational method in ground engineering: principles and applications	R185
Managing materials and components on site	SP146
Tools	
ENGAGE. How to deliver socially responsible construction - a client's guide	C627
Easy access environmental management. Implementation of BS 8555 in the construction sector. Phases 1-3 and 4-7 (CD)	C640
Other publications	
Integrating safety, quality and environmental management	C509
Environmental issues in construction – a strategic review	C510
The reclaimed and recycled construction materials handbook	C513
Environmental management in construction	C533
Demonstrating waste minimisation benefits in construction	C536
The handbook of supply chain management	C546
Sustainable construction: company indicators	C563
Guidance on the costing of environmental pollution from construction	C565
Sustainable construction procurement. A guide to delivering environmentally responsible projects	C571
Habitat translocation – a best practice guide	C600
Design for deconstruction. Principles of design to facilitate reuse and recycling	C607
How much noise do you make? A guide to assessing and managing noise on construction sites	PR70
Waste minimisation and recycling in construction: a review	SP122

CIRIA publications relevant to particular topics are listed in the handbook at the end of each topic and details of all CIRIA publications can be found at: www.ciriabooks.com.

5 Appendix

Toolbox talks

Copies of these toolbox talks from the Construction Confederation listed below can be found on the accompanying CD.

No	Title
1	Spill control
2	Water pollution prevention (fuel & oil)
3	Dust and air quality
4	Noise and vibration
5	Water pollution: silt
6	Water pollution: cement and concrete
7	Tree protection
8	Waste management
9	Storage of waste
10	Japanese knotweed
11	Himalayan balsam
12	Giant hogweed
13	Oil/diesel storage
14	Material handling and housekeeping
15	Archaeology
16	Bentonite
17	Pumping and overpumping
18	Washing down plant and machinery
19	Bats
20	Badgers
21	Be a good neighbour
22	Great crested newts
23	Working on previously developed land
24	Segregation of waste

Appendix 6

Acknowledgements

This second edition of the handbook updates the original Environmental good practice on site (CIRIA C502, 1999), which resulted from CIRIA research project 559. This update has been undertaken by CIRIA in collaboration with a project steering group of industry practitioners. This handbook was designed by CIRIA Publishing.

Funders

This update was funded by the CIRIA Core Programme and the Environment Agency.

Project steering group

CIRIA wishes to express its thanks to the members of the group for their contributions to the work:

Full members

Gareth Brown (chair)	Morrison Construction Services Limited and then Mouchel Parkman
Jonathan Ben Ami	Arup
John Davies	BAA
Ross Fairley	Burges Salmon
Liz Hobday (and colleagues)	Environment Agency
Andrew Kinsey	Bovis Lend Lease
Beverley Lister	BAA Terminal 5 Project
Steve Livingstone	Jackson Civil Engineering
John Peters	Construction Confederation

Corresponding members (provided comments on specific sections)

Gillian Bilsborough	Countryside Council for Wales
Helen Doran	English Nature
Jonathan Essex	WSP Group
Peter Hinton	Institute of Field Archaeologists
Dr Claire Hyland	Environment and Heritage Service NI
Alastair McNeill	Scottish Environment Protection Agency
Ian Nicholson	Responsible Solutions Ltd
Howard Price	Chartered Institute of Environmental Health

CIRIA's project managers for this research were Greg Chant-Hall, Philip Charles and Samantha Connolly.

6 Appendix

Source materials

CIRIA is grateful to the following organisations, who provided information:

Arup
Bovis Lend Lease
Morrison Construction Services Limited
The Construction Confederation Environmental Forum who developed and provided the tool box talks included on the CD accompanying this handbook.

CIRIA would also like to thank the following organisations for providing photographs:

Arup
BAA plc
Bovis Lend Lease
Morrison Construction Services Limited
Scottish Environmental Protection Agency.

Original project acknowledgements

The original work was carried out by Scott Wilson with support from Balfour Beatty. The principal contributors from Scott Wilson were Stuart Coventry and Claire Woolveridge, and from Balfour Beatty, Marcus Pearson. The handbook was designed by Thirst Design and Marketing.

Funders

The research leading to the publication of this handbook was funded by CIRIA Core Programme, the Environment Agency, Sniffer (Scotland & Northern Ireland Forum for Environmental Research) and the National House Building Council.

Project steering group

Members of the original project steering group were:

Andrew Beauchamp (chair)	Connect Roads Ltd
Phil Chatfield	Environment Agency
Trevor Curson	Aspinwall & Co Ltd
Lawrence Emmerson	BAA
Rob Kremis	Tarmac
Arthur Perks	National House building Council
Gerard Sloyan	J Doyle & Co Demolition Ltd
Brent Turton	Westminster City Council
Martin Worthington	AMEC Civil Engineering.

Corresponding members of the project steering group were:

Kelvin Potter	ICI Technology
Ruth Wolstenholme	Scottish Environment Protection Agency
Richard Wright	English Nature.

CIRIA's research manager was Daniel J Leggett.

7 Appendix

Source materials

CIRIA is grateful to the following organisations, which provided information and access to sites:

ACC Archaeology
Costain Civil Engineering Ltd
Rydon Construction
Schal
Tarmac.